SCIENCE AND
WESTERN DOMINATION

By the same author
THE RIDDLE OF THE PYRAMIDS

SCIENCE AND WESTERN DOMINATION

Kurt Mendelssohn F.R.S.

85 illustrations
24 line drawings

READERS UNION
Group of Book Clubs
Newton Abbot 1977

CONTENTS

ACKNOWLEDGMENTS

The author is grateful to his colleagues at the universities of Coimbra and Oporto for making available to him material concerning early Portuguese ocean navigation

CHAPTER ONE

The key to world domination

The noon of the white man's world has passed and the shadows are lengthening rapidly. Five centuries have gone by since the little ships of the Portuguese ventured out to cross the oceans for the first time, and began to turn the world, which had belonged to all the races of mankind, into a white dominion. Only a short while ago it was still possible to talk quite seriously about the white man's burden, when today we hasten to apologize for the mortal sin of colonialism. If tomorrow the white race relinquishes its rule, it will be to the teeming millions of Asia but not to a new idea. The new strength of Asia is vested in a combination of numbers, skill, patience and industry, together with Western science and technology. The tools and weapons before which the whites are now ready to yield are those which they have created themselves. Even the central idea of Communism was enunciated by a German half-Jew who had found refuge in London. The wisdom and the ancient cultures of Asia have as yet made little impression on the Western mind, and the strength on which the present Eastern Renaissance is based bears the stamp 'made in Europe'.

Five hundred years ago, when the ships of Prince Henry the Navigator edged their way along the coast of Africa in the first step towards dominating the world, Europe was desperately poor in comparison with the great civilizations of the East. Soon she was going to be made even poorer by wars and plagues. By then, however, the foundation of Europe's future wealth had been laid. Its roots lay in a single philosophical idea which today is called science, but whose old name, 'natural philosophy', provides a rather better description. In any case, for all but the Anglo-Saxon peoples the term which is equivalent to our 'science' quite generally covers every intellectual achievement, including all those fields which in the English-speaking world are classed as arts subjects. When, for convenience's sake, we refer from now on to 'science', we shall really mean natural philosophy. Its one outstanding feature is, as we shall presently see, a unique economy of effort, and it is this particular economy which has made all the difference between the fate of European man and that of the other races.

One thing should be made abundantly clear before entering on the subject proper. When referring to 'the white man's world' or 'white domination' – and we shall continue to use these terms – this has nothing to do with racialist thinking or with any idea of a cultural superiority of the white race over the contribution made by others. The use and operation of modern science are, one suspects, steps in human evolution which sooner or later would have had to be made anyway. There is no reason to believe that, before this intellectual explosion took place five centuries ago, the great civilizations of the world differed appreciably in the level of intellectual or moral attainment. Even their knowledge of nature was very much the same. Which particular cultural group should have hit upon the method of natural philosophy may have been largely accidental, and this suspicion is reinforced by the fact that, in spite of all efforts to do so, we have been quite unable to discover why it started in the West. All we can say is that it was initiated by a racial group inhabiting Europe whose skin, owing to long prehistoric habitation in Arctic conditions, had lost most of its pigmentation.

What is so spectacular is the rapid rise of science, and its fairly negligible effect on man's moral behaviour. Admittedly, science has offered an enhanced scope for the destruction of life, but it has done the same for its preservation and for the alleviation of suffering. In fact, for what it is worth, the world population has increased. Looking – dispassionately and on a long-term basis – at the influence of science on human relations, it seems to have made remarkably little difference. The reason for this is twofold. First, five centuries is a very short time in human evolution and, secondly, the application of science is limited to a strictly circumscribed area. Science, as we shall presently see, relies on the mathematical correlation of observed phenomena. It therefore has to depend on 'invariant' laws of nature, which means it is confined to conditions that are not unduly influenced by uncontrollable external factors. However, where these conditions exist and science can be applied, it tends to sweep the board, and this is exactly what has happened.

The object of this book is to trace the essential steps in thought that have led along the path of science to white domination over the rest of the world. It is neither a history of science nor an account of scientific achievement, but a history of those concepts and ideas of natural philo-

sophy which have inexorably forced the West into a position of economic superiority. It was an enterprise in which greed came only second to
the spirit of adventure. It is usually said that the rise of modern science
was part of the Renaissance, and we shall have to deal with this facet in
the next chapter. However, for our story the term Renaissance is a
serious misnomer. It has little to do with the resurrection of the spirit
of Graeco-Roman antiquity. Natural philosophy in the modern sense
could not be *re*born because it had not existed before. Instead, it came
into the world as something entirely new, a revolution that has shaped
the lives of more people than any previous idea, the great religions included. Science has provided mankind with a new dimension which is
both terrifying and exhilarating.

Before we can embark on our history of scientific ideas, something has
to be said about the reason why natural philosophy has had this enormous impact on human affairs, which far exceeds the success of any
other philosophical method. Its immense strength lies in its power of
accurate prediction. There is a minimum of fumbling. Trial-and-error
methods are reduced to a level which was quite unknown in former
phases of human activity. An aero-engineer who, applying scientific
principles, designs a new aircraft not only knows, even in the drawing-
board stage, that his aircraft will be capable of flying, but he also can
forecast, with a fair degree of accuracy, its performance. A political
group, planning a new election campaign, does not necessarily meet
with the same degree of success. This disparity has nothing to do with
the complexity of the problem since the aircraft is bound to be infinitely more complex than the party's manifesto. A similar difference in
certainty exists when we consider operation. The aircraft is far more
likely to deliver its occupants via a predetermined route to the required
destination than does an elected government.

Here it must be noted that the predictability of political schemes has
not appreciably improved in the last thousand years or so. It was very
much on the same level at a time when flying appeared an unattainable
dream. Politicians tried and erred then at roughly the same rate as they
are trying and erring today. The remarkable progress of science is thus
merely a relative phenomenon, and it is a matter of taste whether we say
that technological development has advanced or that human society has
lagged behind. What is remarkable, on the other hand, is that the development of the scientific method should have been limited to European man. The amount of political and sociological trial and error in the
great oriental civilizations is of the same order of magnitude as in

Europe, and in all other respects, too, these civilizations compare well with the West.

The fact that Asia has now chosen to deviate from its traditional pattern and to follow the technological road demonstrates, better than any other argument, that the philosophical method of science is the most outstanding contribution which has been made to human progress in the last millennium. Since, for reasons unknown to us, scientific progress has not been matched by a corresponding development in morality, the white race has used this powerful method to dominate the globe. It seems that those who apologize for the latter fact tend to forget the achievement of having developed science in the first place. There is, moreover, no reason to believe that, if another civilization had developed science, it would have desisted from using it for exactly the same purpose.

The advantage which European man gained over the rest of humanity is based on a new method of prediction. The value of this prediction lies not so much in allowing us to see into the future, but in permitting us to exclude many avenues of progress which have no future. The scientific method directs human effort, not by helping us to see farther afield, but by limiting our progress along lines which have a reasonable chance of leading us where we hope to go. Generally speaking, the strength of scientific prediction is of very short range, requiring a new prediction at every new step. As is only natural, the scientist is continually tempted to leap a few steps ahead, and there are very few scientists who have not indulged now and then in hazarding an 'informed guess'. Indeed, without such guesses even science would be dreary, and most of the great advances have been the result of successful guesses. To rely on guesses alone, however, is tantamount to a negation of science. Besides being informed and lucky, successful guesses must be capable of verification in order to be of use in science.

The ability to limit progress to profitable avenues carries in itself that economy of effort which has made science so successful. With a given number of people who are trained for, and capable of, using a particular method, it is clearly of the utmost importance that they should not dissipate their efforts along lines where the method is inapplicable. Accordingly, science enforces a strict discipline in obeying the rules of the game. The rules are such that they ensure economy of effort. We usually call them the laws of nature.

However, the applications of these laws are precisely limited by the phenomena to which they may be applied. Generally, these are the

phenomena of the physical world. Only very gradually are we beginning to express aspects of living matter in natural laws which approach
the predictability of physical laws. Such laws have already been helpful
in agriculture and husbandry, and in the control of disease. But they
become increasingly difficult to formulate as we try to predict the
behaviour of highly developed species, and as yet we can see no immediate hope of applying them to human affairs. The behaviour of the
electorate still remains nothing better than a wild guess, and its reaction
to economic conditions is well beyond the prophetic powers of politicians and economists. On the other hand, in those areas in which we can
formulate strict laws of nature, we can be sure of success; and the
stricter the better. From now on, when we talk about science we will
mean, on the whole, physical science, and we shall severely leave out
such things as 'social science' which must be regarded as a contradiction
in terms.

The fundamental belief on which all science is based is that of an
integral creation. It is tacitly assumed that the universe in all its component parts is interdependent, and that the interdependence should be
unique. Applying loose, but for the moment convenient, terminology,
this means that a particular set of causes can have only one particular
set of effects. The object of science is to discover the nature of this
interdependence. Its strength and success lie in making use of such fragments of interdependence as have already been established. From where
we stand today we can see that this knowledge is very fragmentary
indeed.

The difficulty is that, while the laws of nature have been made by
God, they have to be formulated by man. Such formulation requires a
formula, and the quantities which go into it. Speaking of quantities
presupposes that the idea of a unique interdependence of the constituents
within the universe should be concomitant with the concept of number,
and that the operators in the formula should be the processes of addition
and subtraction, or their developments such as multiplication, division and so on. This supposition is in fact part of the basic belief which
the Greeks already expressed by saying that God is a mathematician.
Whether God is really a mathematician, or whether he has created our
brain in such a way that we see him as a mathematician, is an intriguing
question, but for the purpose of our story we shall, for the rest, accept
the basic belief of a uniquely determined integral creation.

What really interests the scientist, and what we will be mainly concerned with from now on, are the formulations of the laws of nature and

the changes in formulation which have taken place as science has developed. The basic belief in the unique interdependence has gradually grown out of the observation of regularities. Some of these are so obvious that their mention must appear trite, such as the regularity with which day follows night, and the annual periodicity with which the day lengthens and shortens. A quite different and even more obvious regularity is that, whichever way you hold it, the level of water in a jug will always be parallel to the horizon.

The primary object of scientific inquiry is to establish as many of these regularities as possible, and then to reduce their number by trying to find a common explanation for some of them. In most cases this is only partially possible. For instance, while in both the regularities already mentioned the concept of universal gravitation is relevant, it does not suffice. The two laws to which these and many other regularities have been reduced, that of universal gravitation and that of conservation of momentum, were both enunciated by Newton. He was not, however, able to find the ultimate connection which these two laws must have if the belief in unique interdependence is correct. Such a connection was only proposed 250 years later by Einstein, through the concept of general relativity, but we have as yet not sufficient evidence to accept this unifying concept with the same confidence as the two laws of Newton.

There thus exists a secondary object of science, which introduces an element of control by testing the law to which the regularities have been reduced. This can be done either by making observations on a great number of similar regularities or, even better, by investigating corollaries of the law. In the case of general relativity, it is a necessary corollary that a beam of light should deviate from its straight path when passing close by a massive object. Using the sun as the largest mass near at hand, and waiting for an eclipse to reduce its glare, we find that the apparent shift in the position of a star seen close to the sun can just be detected by our most accurate methods of observation. This is the reason why expeditions are sent to remote and usually inconvenient places wherever the rare total eclipses of the sun are due to occur. The evidence which they have brought back from those lucky occasions when they were not foiled by cloud, is as yet inconclusive.

We therefore have two grades of predictability in science. The more direct one deals with cases which have been investigated and used without doubt for safe prediction. If the circuit of an electric torch is closed by pressing the switch, a current will flow and the bulb will light up. This is accepted as quite certain even for a newly assembled, and as yet

unused, torch. If it does not light up at the first attempt, the shop
assistant will look for a manufacturing fault rather than doubt the laws
of nature pertaining to electric currents. The same is true for a new
power station.

The regularities concerning electric currents and their connection with
magnetism were thoroughly investigated in the first half of the nineteenth century, and the laws of nature containing these regularities were
formulated in 1865 by James Clerk Maxwell in a set of differential
equations. These equations were able to account for all known observations and uses of electric currents but, as Maxwell noticed immediately,
they allowed for other phenomena which had never been observed.
From his equations Maxwell predicted the existence of electromagnetic
vibrations, and such waves were eventually produced and detected a
quarter of a century later by Heinrich Hertz. They form the basis of the
whole technique of radio communication, including television.

Maxwell's prediction of radio waves is of a higher grade than the
switching on of the new torch, or the functioning of a new power
station. It goes further than a repetition of known regularities, because
it involves entirely new, and as yet unobserved, regularities. Both sets of
regularities, however, the known and the newly predicted, are inti-
mately connected by the set of differential equations. Provided that
Maxwell's formulation of the laws of electromagnetism was correct,
the existence of radio waves had become as inevitable by this formulation
as the switching on of the torch.

It is not always easy to make a sharp distinction between these two
grades of predictability, since very often the prediction used constitutes
only a small deviation from previously known regularities. Nevertheless,
there is a fairly clear pattern of the operation of the scientific method.
First, regularities are recognized as such and recorded. Then, a formulation is sought which, preferably in the simplest and most general way,
contains these regularities. This then has the status of a law of nature. The
newly formulated law may, and usually will, predict further regularities
which were previously unknown. Finally, the objective is a combination
of two or more of these laws into a still more general formulation. For
instance, the great significance of Einstein's theory of special relativity is
due to the fact that it provides a combination of the electromagnetic
laws with those of mechanics.

It must be noted that in all these stages of using the scientific method
of philosophy, observation plays a most important role. It is the key to
the whole operation, be it in the primary gathering of regularities, or in

their testing, or in the proof of the formulated law. It is thus quite justifiable that some of the early university chairs of physics were established as professorships of experimental philosophy, a term which expresses the occupation of the holders better than the later designation. The key position of the experiment in science is indispensable in that economy of effort which has made science so successful.

In the first place, the experiment sees to it that speculation cannot run riot. When a set of observed regularities is combined into a theory, the next thing to do is to test this theory by experiment. Normally, the next step in speculation is only taken if the experiment has provided confirmation for the correctness of the initial step. Failure to confirm the theoretical prediction requires that the theory be discarded or modified. Very often the nature of the result will indicate in which respect the theory was wrong. It frequently happens that a theoretician will not wait for the experiment, but will go ahead and heap conclusion upon conclusion; but this is definitely bad science. The only justification for such a procedure is that the theoretician may be either very lucky or inspired. Even so, an unchecked sequence of speculations is always a breach of the rules according to which the game should be played, since it is one of the two important functions of the experiment that it should save unnecessary effort. Speculation based on an unchecked theory which subsequently turns out to be wrong is wasted effort, and means uneconomical thinking.

These are the rules of the game, but only too often do they have to be broken legitimately. The theoretician may not be able to wait for the checking experiment for the simple reason that the experiment is too difficult, or too expensive. Wasted theoretical effort, may, in fact, be very much cheaper than the experiment. Nevertheless, the experiment will ultimately have to be performed, whether the taxpayer likes it or not. The interesting stage has now been reached when, as is the case with space research or particle bombardment, the taxpayers of several large countries have to combine their resources in order to get the experiment performed.

The other important function of the experiment is the discovery of new facts, such as the discovery of America which foiled Columbus's experiment to reach the Indies. Here we mean by 'new fact' not one of the suspected regularities, as with Maxwell and the radio waves, but some completely unsuspected phenomena. For instance, at the turn of the century there existed two rival theories according to which the electrical resistance of a metal should either drop gradually to zero, or rise gradually to an infinitely high value as the absolute zero of temperature is approached. A decision had to wait until a method for the close approach of absolute zero had been found. When in 1908 Kamerlingh Onnes in Leyden succeeded in doing this, he immediately performed the experiment and found that the first alternative was almost, if not quite, the correct one. In addition, however, he discovered that most metals will suddenly and completely lose their resistance a few degrees *above* absolute zero. This 'superconductivity' was an entirely new phenomenon which had no place in the earlier predictions. In fact, for a long time it remained unexplained, i.e. it was completely unconnected with any of the known regularities. When such a very isolated new fact is discovered, it always means that we have entered into a new field of natural phenomena of which, up to then, we had no knowledge whatever. At the time of their discovery, nobody could suspect, and therefore predict, the existence of either America or superconductivity.

There is a close and easily understandable connection between new probes and the discovery of previously unsuspected phenomena. America had to wait for the ocean-going ship and its navigational aids, and superconductivity had to remain unrevealed until the liquefaction of helium had given access to the temperature range of a few degrees above absolute zero. Thus there is virtue *per se* in novel methods of exploration, since it can be argued that the opening of new windows is bound to disclose new vistas. Equally, it must be argued that as long as new vistas remain to be discovered, we cannot expect to arrive at the final synthesis of natural laws because our knowledge of the phenomena remains incomplete. The ultimate aim of the scientist is to reach the state where the opening of any new window will only reveal an already well-known view. Then all the pieces of God's jigsaw puzzle will be available, and they will have to fit into one, and only one, picture. That final state of the scientific world will be a Nirvana so perfect that it can have no future.

As it is, we are spared the horror of contemplating too seriously the spectre of such intellectual stalemate. So far, all the new windows into the physical world which man has been able to open have revealed new aspects of it. Sometimes it happens that the view from one window has been thoroughly explored, but inevitably such exploration has also revealed further new windows which have to be opened. The white man's first venture over the uncharted oceans, besides bringing knowledge of new continents, also gave direct proof that the earth is a globe. In our time the exploration of the land surface has been brought virtually to a close, but a sphere holds within its surface a content, and of this content we know next to nothing. Emanating from the interior of the earth there is volcanic heat and a magnetic field of whose cause we are as yet largely ignorant. Little is known about the beds of the oceans, and until quite recently we had not been able to penetrate very far into the atmosphere. Then a new window was opened on that day in October 1957 when the first satellite was launched into outer space. It is indeed fortunate for mankind that such strategic and political importance is being attached to the occupancy of extra-terrestrial space, because the opening of this new window is quite expensive, and weighty reasons have to be advanced to justify it. The mere thirst for knowledge would certainly cut no ice with those who prefer to see the money spent rather for the good of humanity, which means to provide them with three Sundays each week instead of two. Neither will the thirst for knowledge impress those who are adamant that any space programme must wait until equal opportunity can be given to everybody to go to the moon. However, in the face of all those humanitarian and ideological objections, man has set foot on the moon, and in the years to come many questions which have puzzled astronomers and physicists for a long time will be settled by the instruments reporting back from the space ships. It is safe to predict that even more questions will be posed by the strange things which they are going to see.

The experiment requires instruments, and the instruments of science form a most important chapter in this branch of philosophy. The invention of new methods of exploration and measurement is an integral part of the peculiar intellectual adventure which gave the white man command of the earth. The conception and design of a new probe is a feat in science which in importance often parallels the concept of a new abstract idea. It is for this reason that one is inclined to deplore the disappearance of the old term 'experimental philosophy', since the invention of a new probe often goes far beyond the solution of how it can be done. It always also involves the problem of what can be done, which means asking questions. And asking questions, preferably of such a kind as to admit of an answer, is the business of philosophers. When in 1932 Cockroft and Walton built the first particle accelerator, it was a superb exercise in experimental ingenuity, ranging from electrical engineering to high vacuum technique. Yet more important than all this was the guiding idea of building *any* machine which would make atomic nuclei react with each other, a process which does not normally take place in the physical world of our experience.

The probes have two functions: to open up new fields for investigation, and to measure. Since science is concerned with revelations through quantitative relationships, the regularities have to be established by measurement. Sometimes an instrument will combine the two functions, but as often as not the two problems have to be solved separately. Measurement is the recording of numbers which have to be correlated with other numbers obtained in a different measurement but referring to the same event. Galileo, when he established the law of harmonic oscillation, had to count the number of swings of a chandelier in the cathedral. Having no timepiece at his disposal during the service, he correlated this number with a count of his pulse beat. The investigation yielded the unexpected result that the time for each swing was the same, whether the swing was large or small, a fact which has given us all our clocks and watches.

Galileo's observation contains the whole essence of what gave Western man domination over the world; recording of regularities, compounding them into laws of nature, and designing experiments as the basic method of his new philosophy. The recipe is simple, but has turned out to be eminently successful. The question has often been asked why the great civilizations of the East did not develop science and technology. The answer to this question was once given by Einstein, who pointed out that it is the wrong question. The miracle, he said, was not that the East failed to create experimental philosophy, but that the West did. However, why this happened is a riddle that has never been solved. To be candid, we simply don't know. It would indeed be rash to suggest that it was developed merely out of a desire to enslave others. But whether it was intended or not, this is what in the end happened. In addition to greed for riches and domination, the white man became possessed suddenly of a strange spirit of adventure, of an insatiable intellectual curiosity that has driven him on for the past five hundred years. It is this curiosity and this spirit of adventure, in thought as well as in action, to which we will now turn. For the first scene the stage will be set in a little town on the windswept southwestern corner of Europe where nothing remains today – except the name.

No ideas, not even scientific ones, grow in the test tube. They germinate and develop in men's minds, and these minds are conditioned by their environment. Beyond the discoverer's character there is the world into which he is born and bred, and whatever his brain thinks up will be shaped and sharpened by this world. The man and the mould into which he has been cast form an integral part of any new thought which he may contribute. Science is that essential ingredient of Western civilization which distinguishes it from the cultures of others.

Original scientific ideas and concepts are basically the work of individuals rather than the collective effort of many, and the success of our world has for centuries now depended on the achievements of geniuses. That the execution of their ideas may often have to rely on the work of thousands of other people does not alter this fact. We thus have come to regard the leading role of the genius as a necessary and desirable feature of the world, and the names of men like Copernicus, Newton, Faraday and Einstein are deeply imprinted on the mind of the school-child. It is here perhaps, more than in any other respect, that the West differs from the civilizations of the East.

In China or India, regard for the achievement of the individual has been bestowed much more sparingly by society. It has been limited to the rare phenomenon of a great religious leader or a great philosopher. To Eastern peoples, harmony of mankind in general, both with the forces of nature and with each other, has been the main aim of life; an attitude that fights shy of drastic innovation in an accepted pattern of existence. The belief that this pattern, which had been achieved in centuries of patient evolution and self-discipline long ago, must be maintained, contrasts profoundly with the West's obsession with change and progress. The men whose life and work form the subject of this book have never existed in the East because the East would have given them no encouragement.

Now, after rejecting consistently in the centuries past the blandishments of Western science, the Eastern nations have changed their minds and are absorbing, in a somewhat undigested form, the so-called blessings of Western science, from electronics to automatic weapons. Most of them are quite willing to build on this foundation without concerning themselves particularly with its origin. It rarely occurs to Easterners that the West too, might have a history, not only of wars but also of ideas. I know my colleagues in Delhi, Peking and Tokyo well enough to realize that after six p.m., or whenever their day's work is finished, they long to re-immerse themselves into the quiet solace of their own heritage. They simply have not time to bother about the West's. To them this book is dedicated.

CHAPTER TWO

The conquest of the globe

At some time close to the year 1500 Hieronymus Bosch of Aachen painted the enigmatic altarpiece whose name was forgotten long ago, and which we call *The Garden of Delights*. Almost a century later it was acquired by Philip II of Spain, and for the last five years of his life it adorned his apartment in the Escorial. The apartment is a gloomy single room which opens on the high altar of the monastery church to which the lord of the world had retired. They were a strange breed, these Habsburgs who ruled the new age of expanding white domination. As a boy Philip had been taken by his father, the Emperor Charles V, to a lonely place where, in a locked room, an old woman was lying on a bed of straw, with staring eyes and raving mad. 'This', said Charles to his son, 'is your grandmother, Juana *la Loca*.' That was many years before Charles himself handed on the reins of government and retired to the little monastery at Yuste with an old servant and an ape as his companions. He died of a cold, caught at a rehearsal of his own funeral, which had become his favourite pastime in old age. Philip loved the paintings of Hieronymus Bosch, which possibly held a message for the lonely man, a message which has been lost through the centuries. A host of interpretations have been invoked in attempts to explain *The Garden of Delights*. They range from medieval love symbolism to the teaching of a freethinkers' sect, but none of them is very convincing. Only today, as our own era draws to a close, does the picture which was painted at its birth seem to acquire meaning once again.

The closed doors of the triptych show the world, a transparent globe holding a flat earth surrounded by water. The earth is covered with luxuriant tropical plants, such as the discoverers had just brought back from lands beyond the oceans. The insides of the doors represent Paradise and Hell in the usual manner, but the treatment is far from traditional. They are of the same eerie surrealist beauty as the main picture. This centre panel shows man in a hundred ways, naked, stylized and without individuality, engaged in a great variety of actions. Some of these we can understand, but others appear to have no meaning at all. It is not only the fantasy and imagination which convey such a strong sense of the unreal but, even more, the dreamlike quality of the whole scene. Man seems to move in a trance, acting automatically at the command of an unseen power; a world of earthly delights without joy. The soul appears to have been freed from the fetters of medieval religious life, and is entering a new, and as yet unknown, world. In the distance we see the shape of odd and frightening structures, gigantic blue spheres which look like monstrous alembics or grotesque machines of war. In the sky above, man has taken wing, soaring towards the sun.

It is difficult to imagine the painting on any altar of the Christian faith, and we have no indication for whom or for what purpose it was painted. Perhaps it was just that, gifted with the power to see into the future, Hieronymus Bosch set down the prophecy of the new age into which he had been born. Even as he was painting, the crystal sphere which had enclosed the world of man since antiquity was shattered by a young priest living on the Baltic coast. In Italy Leonardo da Vinci was exploring the mechanism of the human body, and Alexander VI, Rodriguez Borgia, the most worldly of all popes, had divided up the world into two hemispheres. Amerigo Vespucci realized that 'the Indies' so recently discovered by Columbus were actually a new continent, and he was rewarded by the German cartographer Waldseemüller who named the new world America. But for this, we would know Amerigo only as the uncle of the girl who was the model for Botticelli's Venus, born from the sea.

Indeed, the earth of Europe had suddenly become a garden of delights. After a millennium of rest and stagnation the white race was bursting into that frenzy of activity called the Renaissance. What exactly brought about this change is not at all clear. After the collapse of the Roman empire and the attendant great migrations, European man had lapsed into that long period of inactivity which modern historians call the Dark Ages, no doubt because it was free of major wars. Out of the disintegration of the classical world an entirely new culture had arisen, based on the teaching of Christ. Man lived at peace with himself and – on the whole – also with his neighbour. The crystal sphere of his world, which he had inherited from the Greeks, was fairly small and he was at its centre. Moreover, it was clear from Holy Writ that this world had been created only a few thousand years ago, and was likely to come to an end fairly soon. There was thus little reason to look upon earthly existence as anything more than a transitory stage, a preparation for the eternal life to come. Man's chief aim was to live a pious life full of good deeds or, failing that, to atone for misdeeds so that he was permitted to enter the Kingdom of Heaven. On the other hand, not much good was to be expected from any change in the manner of the earthly life and, instead of exploring the surrounding world with its phenomena, man's mind was centred on his soul. Christ's warning, 'What profits man if he gains the whole world but lose his soul,' determined the spirit of the Middle Ages.

There is a strong similarity between medieval life in Europe and that of China up till the twentieth century. The Chinese, too, felt that they had discovered the secret of true life: man was to obey the precepts of honesty and decency in order to live in harmony with the forces of nature. The Emperor, like the Pope, was the mediator between man and the powers of the universe. Like the Christians, the children of Han also only knew one world, their world, whose fringes were peopled with barbarians. These were inferior unfortunates from whom enlightenment had been withheld. As time passed, they too would find the true way of harmonious living. To introduce a change in the institutions of society would only imperil the continuance of this harmony, and that had to be avoided at any price. As the ideal form of existence had been found, there could be no progress. Calamities such as floods, drought or invasion by barbarians were merely signs that the mandate of Heaven had been withdrawn from the reigning family, and that a change of dynasty was indicated.

However, whereas the Chinese went on adhering to the pattern of stability until their world was upset by white intrusion, Europe suddenly entered upon a new phase of human activity without apparent coercion from outside. The fact that several theories have been advanced to explain the phenomenon of the Renaissance, and that these theories are all equally plausible, clearly shows that we are as yet in ignorance of the true explanation. Both urbanization and the invention of gunpowder have been blamed, but Constantinople had been a large Christian town for a thousand years before the Renaissance, and it seems that the first guns were fired by the Moors. Altogether it must seem unlikely that such a profound change from a condition of static tranquillity could have been brought about by some marginal issue.

At about AD 1400, and for some unknown reason, Western man lost his confident belief in life after death which had sustained him throughout the Middle Ages, and he has found nothing to replace it. With doubts arising as to the certainty of an eternal life, life on earth acquired a new significance. Instead of patiently walking through it towards the gate of death, every minute of the short span of earthly existence became of importance. This loss of tranquillity brought with it a new awareness of the phenomena of nature. Since he was no longer sure that he would be triumphant after death, man had to triumph in this life. He had to show his mastery over the forces of nature and over other men. Perhaps this is the true meaning of the strange trance into which the human shapes in *The Garden of Delights* seem to have fallen. Perhaps this was the true meaning which had revealed itself to Philip II as he sat brooding over the world, one hemisphere of which belonged to him. The age of white domination had begun.

The first manifestation of the new age was the seaborne exploration of the globe by the Portuguese, who lived at the very edge of the limitless ocean. It started in 1418 with a series of African expeditions organized by Prince Henry the Navigator, and was essentially concluded a century later with the first circumnavigation of the earth by Magellan's ship. The whole project, which included the opening of the sea route to India, was brilliantly organized and of enormous scope. It can rank as the equal of any modern large-scale efforts in exploration, such as the release of nuclear energy or the probing of outer space. The astonishing feature is the foresight with which the required forces were marshalled, and the necessary resources developed. The one-masted ship, which had been inherited from antiquity and had remained virtually unchanged throughout the Middle Ages, was replaced by three-masted caravels of quite new design which permitted much higher speeds and much greater versatility. New navigational aids for finding the ship's position were developed, and the compass was improved. Most impressive of all was the strategic support of the venture by building up at the base a strong mathematical and astronomical department, to which also a staff of cartographers was attached. The navigators soon learned to rely very largely on these theoreticians at the base and, as we shall see, their decision determined any major project undertaken by the Crown.

It is one of the miracles of the Renaissance that, in this first great project of exploration, a pattern was set which is so perfect in its design that it has undergone little variation in the following centuries. We must not confuse this new form of sustained exploration with individual travel. Many of the places which the Portuguese eventually reached were known and had been described before. Since the days of the brothers Polo many travellers had made their way along the caravan routes of Asia, or had sailed with the Arab coastal traffic to India and the Orient. The Portuguese venture was completely different both in kind and in extent. It used a new method of transport – ocean travel with large ships – which was free from interference. This was to bypass the hazardous overland routes which were continually subject to robbery, sudden closure, and to the rapacious caprices of tribute-exacting chieftains. It also involved the setting up of a chain of naval bases which had to be fortified, defended and partly settled by Portuguese. The Portuguese wanted a trade route which was reliable and, in order to achieve that, it had to be securely under their control. The whites were from now on going to trade entirely on their own terms. The races with whom they traded soon ceased to be treated as equals: they began to be dominated, and this domination was to be gained by a conscious exploitation of the forces of nature. The conquest of the high seas, the exploration of the trade winds, the ability to determine the nautical position, and knowledge of the distribution of land and water over the globe, together with the possession of superior arms, were all necessary for the establishment of this domination.

The legacy of the Middle Ages provided a convenient moral justification for this intrusion into the non-European territories: the spreading of the Gospel amongst the heathen and the redemption of their souls. Historians, and particularly those of the Protestant countries, have always been inclined to regard the missionary efforts of the Conquistadors as a superb feat of hypocrisy, but this is probably a bit unjust. The Spanish successors of Columbus in particular were not yet deeply imbued with the spirit of the Renaissance, and were essentially still men of the Middle Ages. An eye-witness, Bernal Diaz, has recorded how Cortés, after ascending for the first time the 114 steps of the great pyramid of Mexico, suggested to his chaplain, Father Olmedo, that it might be a good thing to overturn the heathen idols and to erect the cross forthwith. It was left to the more cautious Father to point out the danger, and he expressed his fear that Montezuma might not be as eager to embrace salvation as Cortés assumed. If even a man as sophisticated as Cortés was so intent upon the Christianizing aspect of the conquest, we can hardly deny to his uneducated followers a fair measure of self-righteous missionary spirit in their dealings with the Indios.

The Portuguese, who were much closer to the spirit of the new age, were less ardent in their efforts at Christianization. Their main object clearly was trade. The first exchange of words on landing in India is faithfully recorded in Vasco da Gama's journal. A man who was under sentence for some misdemeanour during the voyage was sent ashore first, and found an inhabitant who could speak Spanish. This, incidentally, was a Jew from Poznan who had come by the land route. The Jew asked the convict what the Portuguese wanted and was told: 'We are looking for Christians and spices.' The reply, too, is recorded in the journal. It was short and to the point: 'Go to hell:' Needless to say, it was not heeded.

However, besides the search for spices, the Portuguese revealed a deep love of adventure, exploration and scientific investigation, without which the grand project would never have succeeded. Indeed, the generally accepted idea that ocean travel and the search for new trade routes were caused directly through the closing of the overland trade by the Turks is not entirely convincing. Portuguese ships began serious exploration in the second decade of the fifteenth century, whereas Constantinople was conquered by the Turks only in 1453. Moreover, there are records prior to that date of ocean navigation which came close to a discovery of America. There was clearly more to the great Portuguese voyages than just the quest for trade. The speculations of the Greek philosophers had left open a great many questions concerning the globe on which we live, and the men of the dawning Renaissance were to get the answers – by going there and seeing for themselves. In order to appreciate the problems they faced, we must survey briefly what was known before they set out, and how this knowledge had been obtained.

In the sixth century BC Pythagoras taught that the earth is round. He may have come to this conclusion by observing the circular shape of the earth's shadow when it eclipsed the moon, or he may simply have postulated this shape because the sphere is the most perfect body. In any case, the roundness of the earth has never been seriously doubted by learned men since his time. Later, Greek geographers concluded that the earth would be uninhabitable at the poles because of extreme cold, and equally uninhabitable near the equator because of great heat. Some, in fact, maintained that no knowledge could ever be obtained about the southern hemisphere since access to it would be prevented by the equatorial heat belt, where the ocean was kept boiling by the rays of the sun. They thought of their own world as a mass of land embracing the Mediterranean and the Black Sea, and believed that this land mass was surrounded by an impassable ocean. For reasons of symmetry a similar land mass was supposed to be located in the southern hemisphere, and a world map of this kind is given 1500 years later in one of the Marco Polo manuscripts.

The problem of the heat belt was the first to be attacked by the Portuguese. They systematically worked their way south along the western coastline of Africa, carefully making maps of their discoveries as they advanced by stages. The limit of the known coastline was the ominous 'Capo de non' at the southern border of present-day Morocco, so called because none of the voyagers who had rounded it had ever returned. It was passed in 1421, but the coast south of it showed a discouraging aspect. The heat increased with diminishing latitude, and the country increasingly resembled the uninhabitable desert predicted by the Greek geographers. However, the Portuguese sailors persisted in their quest until the turning-point was reached in 1445, when Dias discovered the River Senegal and passed Cape Verde. The desert was at an end and human habitation began again. Ten years later Portuguese sailed up the Gambia, and in 1457 they had reached the tenth parallel. Most important of all, south of Cape Verde the African coast began to fall back increasingly towards the east, and when in 1460 Prince Henry died, he must have known that the sea route to India had become a possibility which could be seriously considered.

Judged by present-day standards, Henry must rank as one of the most outstanding of all scientific organizers. Besides being a scholar of renown, he conceived and planned an enterprise of exploration for which no model existed. With great foresight and resourcefulness he methodically developed all the various services which his plan required, and he followed it with incredible persistence and tenacity. Hand in hand with the early African expeditions Henry pursued another line of exploration about which we are less well informed because it seems to have been attended by a good deal of secrecy. This was the probing of the Atlantic Ocean towards the west. Its most important result was the discovery of the Azores, probably in 1432, an event which was of great importance for the plan suggested many years later by Columbus.

In 1419 Henry settled at Sagres at the southwest corner of Portugal. Close to his palace he built a village with houses for his scholars and an observatory. Today nothing is left of Sagres, but even a century after Henry's death, when it was destroyed by Drake's guns, the scholars had already left long before. This research establishment was the base from which all operations were directed for the rest of his life. The nerve centre in which the plans were made and progress was plotted, it was evidently surrounded by a veil of secrecy and very little is known about it. Its head was Maestro Jacomo de Majorca, of whom more will be said later. Competent scholarship seems to have been the sole principle according to which Henry selected his staff. Besides a number of Jews there were even some Spanish Moors, notwithstanding the fact that Henry himself had fought against the Moors at Ceuta. The great improvements in navigation, map-making and ship design which formed the backbone of Portuguese exploration all seem to have emanated from the research institute of Sagres. At the same time experiments were carried out in the nearby shipyard of Lagos, and these resulted in the development of the caravel.

The sailing-ship was invented by the ancient Egyptians more than five thousand years ago. Even before, in prehistoric times, the early dwellers on the Nile found that the easiest way to navigate was to let the boat drift downstream when they wanted to travel northward. Going in the opposite direction, they discovered that a leafy branch held up in the craft would take it upstream on the prevailing northerly winds. By 3000 BC they were constructing sizeable ships with one mast in the middle and steering them with large paddles. For the next four and a half thousand years, peoples of many nations built all kinds of ships without, however, making a basic advance on the Egyptian prototype. Their vessels still had one mast and were steered by rudders at the side.

While this was good enough for the Mediterranean galley or the Hanseatic cog, plying in fairly confined waters, the vast oceans with as yet unexplored wind patterns presented quite new navigational problems. An entirely novel type of ship had to be created to meet the new challenge. In addition to endurance, speed and seaworthiness, versatility became the chief requirement. The result was the caravel, a ship with three masts, carrying lateen sails fore and aft and having a square-rigged main mast. The large mainsail provided a high average speed to cover long distances within reasonable time, while the lateen sails enabled the vessel to cruise against the wind. Thus the caravel allowed the navigators not only to journey to far distant parts, but also to get back again to port against adverse winds. Manœuverability was much increased by attaching a central rudder to the stern post, and at the same time greater stability was achieved by widening the after-castle and making the ship lie fairly low in the water. The slender bow allowed the caravel to cut well through the ocean waves, and her draught was fairly shallow to enable coastal reconnaissance and entering the mouth of rivers.

After millennia of comparative stagnation in ship design, the development of the caravel in evidently a remarkably short time must appear

Fig. 1. *Ocean navigation was made possible by the invention of the many-masted ship in the fifteenth century, particularly by the Portuguese caravel. This woodcut comes from the 'Epistola Christofor Columbi' (published 1494). The foremast is obscured by the mainsail.*

impressive. Almost nothing is known about the stages by which the final form of the vessel was reached. Like the other activities of the Sagres establishment, the construction and trial of its ships were kept secret. However, the combination of new essential features and its ultimate success indicate careful and sound scientific planning with a minimum of fumbling. The close proximity of Lagos to Sagres, and the relative isolation of this small port, made it the ideal trial ground for Prince Henry's naval experiments. Lagos became the first port for the voyages of exploration until, after Henry's death, the research establishment and the naval base were moved to Lisbon.

Henry was the fifth son of King John I of Portugal and Princess Philippa of Lancaster. He was a tall, well-made, fair-haired man with unbounded energy and single-minded purpose. The enterprise required very extensive funds, and a good deal of Henry's efforts must have been directed towards raising the money for his expeditions. After his death there was a temporary lull in the voyages, no doubt due to financial reasons, but in 1469 King Alfonso V, Henry's nephew, granted the African trade to the wealthy merchant Fernando Gomes under the condition that a further three hundred miles of coastline had to be explored every year. Gomes, who probably took over Henry's organization, at first made astonishing progress. As his ships moved into the Gulf of Guinea the results were most encouraging, because the coastline stretched due east at roughly 5° northern latitude. This was exactly in accordance with the Greek idea that the land mass was confined to the northern hemisphere. The sea route to India now seemed within easy reach. However, the triumph was short-lived. At the Cameroons the coast turned south again and when, after five years, the contract lapsed, no eastward trend had been discovered. On the other hand, a southern latitude of 2° had been reached safely, which showed that men could pass through the equatorial region.

The discouraging shape of the African coastline delayed further exploration for another eight years, after which the voyages were resumed with great determination by Alfonso's son, King John II. Five more years of discoveries culminated in the famous voyage of Bartolomeo Dias in 1487. We have reason to assume that Dias no longer bothered to follow laboriously the African coast. He seems to have left it on reaching the Gulf of Guinea, and to have steered across the open seas towards the Congo. He then explored the coast, which still tended mainly south, until he reached a small harbour, the present-day Luderitz, at a southern latitude of about 27°. As he left, a terrific gale sprang up which drove his ships due south for thirteen days. As they were blown helplessly over the uncharted ocean, Dias and his men noted that the tropical heat now gave place to a bitter cold. They realized that they were approaching the Antarctic pole of the earth.

When finally the storm abated, Dias set his course due east in order to regain the African coast. However, once again many days passed and nothing was seen but the cold inhospitable ocean of the south. By dead reckoning Dias concluded that they should have made land long ago unless they had unwittingly doubled the southern tip of Africa. He decided to sail north, and eventually reached the coast again at Mossel-baai. But now it ran due east. Although his crew was utterly exhausted, he pressed on for another 350 miles until he got to the Great Fish River, where the coast took a clear northeastern trend. The sea route to India now lay open, and Dias turned back, passing on his way the cape which on his return was named by King John the Cape of Good Hope – of sailing to India.

The first great step in the history of white domination had been taken. The Europeans had braved the open seas, the heat belt and Antarctic cold. They had established bases along the coast of an alien continent many times the size of their own, and they were well on the way to becoming the masters of the known world. And what they did not yet know, they were prepared to discover and to make subservient to themselves. The stout-hearted Portuguese sailors had little fear of death, but their valour would have come to nought but for the clever brains and the mysterious hidden power which directed their efforts.

The great voyages of discovery have become a standard chapter in our school books, but nothing is said and very little is known about the men who planned and directed them. In a world of Christian zeal they had reasons to remain in the shadow – because they were Jews. Their importance arises from the fact that the Jews held in trust the learning of classical antiquity.

The foundations of western scientific thought were laid by the Greek philosophers of the pre-Christian era. The sum total of knowledge propounded by them is enormous and contains many of the theories which became the working hypotheses for the scientists of the Renaissance, and of the seventeenth century. However, the Greeks made astonishingly little use of what they had discovered and, moreover, in the tests of their theories they generally preferred to rely on argument rather than on experimental proof. Also, we must not forget that for every Greek theory which turned out to be correct in later centuries there are several others which stated contrary views, and which have since proved completely useless and misleading. Thus, while Democritus taught that matter is made up of atoms, Aristotle insisted on a mixture of four elements, each of which had the nature of a structureless fluid. Even so, the Greeks were in command of mathematical descriptions, such as Euclid's geometry, which have remained unchanged through the millennia. Added to this was an impressive catalogue of astronomical data, as well as some simple laws of hydraulics and mechanics. But although the Greeks where thus possessed of an ardent spirit of research and the wish to investigate the nature of the physical world, they did not employ this knowledge in an attempt to dominate others. On the contrary, the only recorded instance of the application of science to war is the effort made by Archimedes of Syracuse in the defence of his native city. There is little doubt that most accounts of his defensive measures, such as the burning of the besiegers' ships with rays of the sun concentrated by mirrors, are wildly exaggerated. In any case, Syracuse was taken by the Romans and Archimedes was slain, as so often happens in war, by mistake.

From the third century B C onward, Greek scientific and mathematical teaching moved to Alexandria where it enjoyed the patronage of the Ptolemaic dynasty. It flourished there well into the first century of our era and a certain, if small, section of Greek knowledge was handed on in Latin translation to the Roman contemporaries. A good deal of this was passed on to educated Romans by their Greek tutors, though very often in a form which was far less accurate than the original statements of the Alexandrian scholars. In this way the detailed arguments of Greek science were gradually lost, and only the bare outlines remained. The process of vulgarization went on through the later centuries of the Roman empire and no fresh knowledge was added. Beside the Roman lack of aptitude in scientific research there was a growing disinclination among the Christianized intelligentsia to bother about the physical world. Thus in the end there was nothing left by the early Middle Ages but a very garbled version of some Greek teaching in incompetently latinized form. Later some further translations were added, but only of well-known and well-tried philosophers, such as Aristotle. Natural philosophy had in the Middle Ages become a closed chapter of human endeavour, a historical phase with Aristotle as the acknowledged authority, even though he classed the flies with the four-legged animals.

But although the days of Greek science had ended, its results had not been lost. It lived on in the Arab world of North Africa, where it was treasured, and spread with the expansion of Islam. It was taught in the Near East, in Sicily, and had gone with the Moorish invasion into Spain. As the Middle Ages drew to a close, the Greek heritage was still available to the West, but unfortunately Greek had become an almost forgotten language and virtually nobody in the Christian world could read Arabic or Syriac – nobody except the Jews who, after the diaspora, had settled in many countries of the Mediterranean area. In the Islamic cities their communities were free from the Christian persecution, and they lived on fairly amicable terms with the Moslem population. Jewish and Moorish scholars communicated freely, and they also kept in constant touch with their co-religionists in Italy and France.

As the Moors were gradually driven from Castile, many of the Jews remained. Shortly before the fall of Toledo a number of Jewish scholars had assisted their Moorish colleagues in drawing up an important set of astronomical tables. In the thirteenth century the King of Castile, Alfonso the Wise, had these translated into Spanish by Rabbi Judah ben Moses Cohen and other Jewish savants, and for the following two centuries the Alfonsine Tables remained the standard almanac. They were soon followed by a great number of other Arab and Greek scientific works dealing with astronomical instruments, clocks and alchemy. Incidentally, the Toledo synagogue and the Jewish communities in Naples and Provence are to be credited with the translation of all important Greek and Arab philosophical and scientific texts into Spanish, Italian and French. Translations of these works in turn into Latin subsequently furnished the scholars of the Renaissance with much of their knowledge of classical thought. The Jews thus formed the bridge over which the Greek heritage was passed on to Western learning.

Far from being mere translators, the Jews had, under Moslem domination, taken a leading part in the further development of Greek scientific ideas, and made important contributions to mathematics, astronomy, physics, alchemy and medicine. The device invented by Rabbi Jacob ben Makhir, and described in Latin in 1342 by Levi ben Gershom, became of particular importance to the early Portuguese discoverers. This was an instrument with which the altitude of the sun or a star could be determined aboard ship, and which became known as Jacob's Staff. It was far less cumbersome and more robust than the astrolabe or the quadrant, and the sailors found it easy and simple to use.

Another half-way house between the Moslem and Christian worlds was the Balearic islands which, after the defeat of the Moors, had come under the crown of Aragon. The inhabitants of the islands were of

necessity a seafaring people, and the members of the Jewish community
of Majorca became the most famous map-makers in the world. Their
most distinguished representative was Abraham Crescas, who lived at
the end of the fourteenth century and who held the official title of
'Master of Maps and Compasses'. Prince John of Aragon calls him 'Jew
of our house' and in 1381, as a mark of his favour, he conferred on
Abraham the right of establishing a public bath. Abraham and his son
Jahuda made for the Prince the famous 'mappamundi', the map of the
world which was the first of its kind in which the scale chart was incorporated. This was the earliest attempt at giving true proportions to the
lands outside the Mediterranean, superseding the medieval world maps
which were nothing better than vague pictorial representations.

After Abraham's death the dignity of 'Map and Compass Jew' was
inherited by Jahuda, who then was summoned to Barcelona and, under
the increasing pressure of forced Christianization, was baptized under the
name Jayme Ribes. Later he accepted an invitation by Prince Henry
the Navigator to come to Portugal, where we have already met him
under the name of Maestro Jacomo of Majorca, as first director of
Henry's famous research institute at Sagres.

In spite of the wave of intolerance and the expulsion of the Jews, first
from Spain and then from Portugal, the direction of geographical ex-
ploration in Portugal and also in Spain remained in the hands of the
Jewish school of theoreticians. Some of them emigrated to North
Africa, but most accepted baptism and stayed. These converts called
Marraños, who quite often retained their Jewish way of life, became an
important and influential section of Portuguese and Spanish society.
Some even rose to high office in the Church, like the scholarly Diego de
Deza who became Inquisitor General. It was Deza who introduced
Columbus to the Jewish mathematician Abraham Zacuto, professor at
the university of Salamanca, and chief adviser on questions of astronomy
and navigation to Ferdinand and Isabella. His pupil Joseph Vecinho, also
a Jew, held the same place under John II of Portugal which Jahuda
Crescas had occupied under Henry the Navigator. He was the leading
theoretician of the Portuguese exploration scheme. The research institute had meanwhile moved to Lisbon, and Vecinho's chief assistant was
the mathematician Moses. When the Jews were expelled from Spain,
Vecinho and Moses were joined by Zacuto.

Of this first great scientific effort in the history of white domination
we know practically nothing except the final achievements – the successful voyages and names of those who undertook them. But we can form

The Garden of Delights, painted at the end of the fifteenth century, may have represented Hieronymus Bosch's vision of man entering upon a new age.

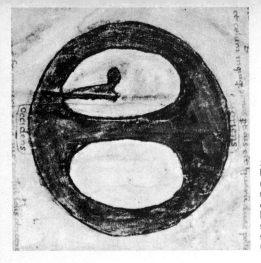

2 Mappamundi from the book of Marco Polo (1254?–1324). In the thirteenth century the earth was believed to have a northern and a southern continent, separated by a boiling tropical ocean.

3, 4 *Right*, Prince Henry the Navigator (1390–1460) of Portugal. Henry, the grandson of John, Duke of Lancaster, inaugurated a secret research establishment at Sagres. The statue overlooks the harbour at Lagos, near by, where the caravel was developed. After his death the geographical research centre was moved from Sagres to the monastery at Belem, near Lisbon (*below*).

5 The tower at the mouth of the Tagus, near Belem, from which the explorers set out on their voyages.

6, 7 *Above*, the scientific armillary sphere (an instrument for establishing latitude) adopted as his royal device by King Manuel the Fortunate (1469–1521) of Portugal. The ropes and anchors (*left*) of Manueline architecture were inspired by the sea route to India.

8 *Below*, The Portuguese fortress of Elmina on the Gold Coast was built in 1482 as a strongpoint and port for the slave trade.

9, 10, 11 The world in which Columbelieved. *Above*, the globe of Martin
Behaim (1459–1506) shows the suppo
close proximity of the eastern and
western shores of the Old World,
leaving no space for America or the
Pacific Ocean. The 1508 map of Afric
(*left*), on the other hand, demonstrate
how well the Portuguese scientists ha
plotted the coastline, and a map from
early sixteenth-century *Chronicle* (*belo*
shows that they knew of the existence
of the Antarctic continent, not
rediscovered till after Cook's voyages
in the eighteenth century.

an opinion of the difficulties which had to be overcome before the globe could be explored and charted. The cardinal problem of determining the position of a ship on the high seas has already been mentioned. In order to solve it, there had to be astronomical tables giving the height of the sun at noon or of the Pole Star for every latitude. With the aid of these, and of instruments such as the Jacob's Staff or the quadrant, the sailors were able to find out whether their ship was in the northern or the southern hemisphere, and its distance from the equator. The theoreticians not only provided the tables but also a number of astronomical instruments, derived from the complicated astrolabes but simplified to such an extent that ordinary ship's captains could be persuaded to use them. Fortunately, a set of instructions has survived which the Portuguese theoreticians prepared for the use of these devices by sailors. The first caution impressed upon them is to note that the Pole Star is not exactly at the celestial North Pole, but that its height varies slightly through twenty-four hours. The pilot is further told how to handle the quadrant in order to make an accurate observation. Many of the instruments were not only calibrated in degrees, but also the names of important landmarks, such as capes, islands or ports, were engraved at the corresponding divisions of the scale. Thus to a very large extent the navigators of the Portuguese relied on the theoreticians. Here again it seems that the information was kept secret. It is significant that the Spanish navigators calculated their voyages on the assumption that each degree of latitude amounted to fifty miles, while the Portuguese captains were issued with sailing instructions based on the correct figure of seventy miles. This difference is important for an understanding of Columbus's claim that India could be reached by a voyage to the west.

Although there are occasional references to 'cosmographers' accompanying the voyages, it seems that this was not usually the case. The work of the theoreticians was confined to their activities at the home research establishment. There is, however, one notable exception – the voyage of Joseph Vecinho along the Guinea coast as far south as Fernando Po in 1485. The object was a careful determination of the height of the sun, extended to the immediate neighbourhood of the earth's equator. The simplest and most reliable latitude determination was the observation of the Pole Star. However, as the equator was crossed, the Pole Star disappeared from sight and the navigators had to rely on the circumpolar constellations of the southern hemisphere, such as the Southern Cross, with which they were unfamiliar. Worse still, there is no Pole Star in the southern sky. Observation of the sun's height, to-

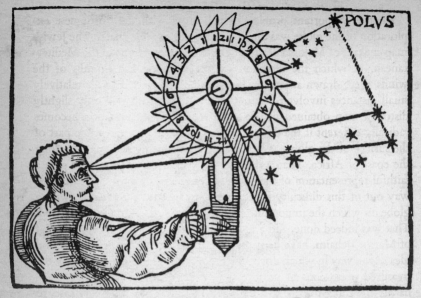

Fig. 2. The nocturnal was an instrument enabling the navigator to determine time at night by sighting against the Pole Star and the Plough.

gether with the use of almanac tables, thus became of prime importance. We can now understand why Vecinho himself had set out to make the observations at the equator.

There is a good deal of evidence that Vecinho was accompanied on this purely scientific expedition by Martin Behaim ('the Bohemian') from Nuremberg, who became famous for the early globe which bears his name. Behaim, too, was probably of Jewish extraction. This voyage was undertaken in connection with the new astronomical tables which Vecinho was preparing for the use of the Portuguese sailors. They were based on the *Almanach Perpetuum* which his teacher, Abraham Zacuto, had published twelve years earlier in Salamanca. Vecinho translated the Hebrew original into Latin and Spanish, and also supplemented the tables with his own observations, eventually putting them into a simplified form which could be understood and applied by the navigators. This manual, *Regimento do Estrolabio e do Quadrente*, which was specially prepared for the use of pilots, contains simplified latitude tables in addition to the instructions for making observations mentioned above.

Another important problem which arose with the Portuguese exploration of the globe was the preparation of suitable charts. The Jewish map-makers of Majorca dealt mainly with sailing charts of the Mediterranean, in which the directions of the compass, the rhumbs of the winds, were drawn as straight lines on a plane sheet. For the relatively small distances involved, the curvature of the earth will only slightly distort a map obtained in this way. However, the situation becomes radically different if the distances begin to cover an appreciable part of the surface of the globe, as in the case of the Portuguese voyages along the coast of Africa. Then a flat sheet of paper can clearly never give a faithful representation of the seas and continents on earth. The obvious way out of this difficulty is, of course, to substitute a flat map with a globe on which the important features of the earth's surface are charted. That was indeed done, and a number of these early globes, such as that of Martin Behaim, have been preserved. From these we can get a good idea of the way in which discovery progressed. These globes, usually the treasured possessions of princes, were both costly and cumbersome – hardly the thing to give to a pilot as a navigational aid. In any case, to be of use, a globe which could be used as a navigational chart would have to be enormous.

Thus a chart had to be devised which, while it could not be a faithful representation of the curved surface of the earth, giving only a distorted image of continents and oceans, should be distorted in a way which provided maximum usefulness. The problem was successfully tackled by another Marraño, Pedro Nuñez, who became Vecinho's successor as head of the Portuguese research establishment. He based his work on a digest of Ptolemy's *Amalgest*, which had been published in the thirteenth century as *Sphaera Mundi* by an Englishman, John Holywood, who called himself Sacrobosco. The sailors were accustomed to read their charts by the use of straight lines drawn on to them, the rhumbs or directions of the winds. Nuñez, in his famous treatise on the sphere, succeeded in finding a simple geometric representation of the globe on a flat sheet of paper in which the rhumbs could be drawn. His way of dealing with the problem was to look downwards on the earth from high above the pole. His chart of the northern or southern hemisphere was therefore simply a circle, the equator, with the pole at its centre. In such a diagram the meridians are radii, i.e. straight lines from the centre of the circle to its circumference, and Nuñez showed that the rhumbs had now become spiral lines between pole and equator, each intersecting the meridians always at the same angle.

Man had now learned to live on a globe instead of a flat world, and Nuñez had demonstrated that the customary manner in which one finds one's way – by using a plane map – could be retained under the new conditions. His work also yielded strange revelations, such as the unexpected fact that the shortest route between two places on the globe is the largest circle by which you can join them. Even today the air traveller is often surprised when he finds that the quickest way from London to Southern California leads through Labrador.

Mercator improved Nuñez' type of chart by using the well-known cylindrical projection in which the rhumbs again become straight lines, but at the expense of greatly distorting the geographical features. Various other projections have been used since, but all these variations and improvements, as well as the perfecting of navigational instruments, have added little in comparison with the great advance made by the Portuguese.

Even before Nuñez wrote his book, the earth had been circled by Magellan's ship, the *Vitoria*. With the exception of Australia and the Antarctic continent, the main features of the distribution of land and sea on earth had been discovered. Command of the high seas, knowledge of the globe, and the advantage which this command and this knowledge gave to the white race had been gained by the use of a new method of thought – science.

Since we are concerned with the development of this method and its concepts, and not with the history of exploration, the discovery of America would require no more than a brief mention were it not that this discovery was made by mistake. As everybody knows, Columbus set out to open the western sea route to India, and if America had not been in his way, that would have been the last the world would have heard of him. He and his three little ships would have perished miserably in that vast ocean he was hoping to cross.

The discovery of the New World is an example of the power of the new experimental approach begun in the Renaissance. Here was a man who by the standards of his time, and indeed of our own, was an adventurer and a bit of a charlatan. His quest was based on a totally erroneous hypothesis but, nevertheless, it paid off. When Columbus returned triumphantly from his first voyage with strange men, animals and plants, nobody was more surprised than the Portuguese geographers and mathematicians, but they realized immediately that he could not have been to India. Even so, there was a lesson for them to learn; in science, exploration, and not just logic alone, can bring rewards, even if

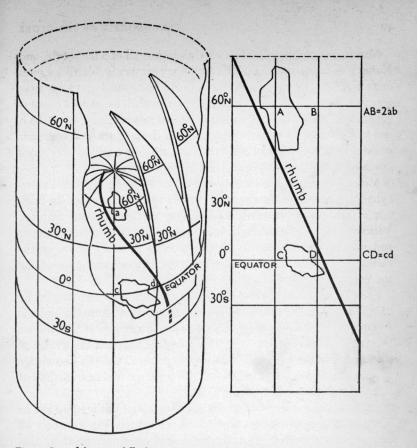

Fig. 3. One of the main difficulties in ocean navigation was the representation of features on the curved surface of the earth on a plane chart. One solution, still frequently used today, was provided in 1569 by Mercator, who transferred global features onto a cylinder.

it is based on a wrong theory. In the history of science the same thing has happened over and over again, from the search for the Philosophers' Stone to the discovery of radioactivity and nuclear fission.

It is an irony of fate that, whereas we know next to nothing about the Portuguese scientists who shaped the pattern of the new age, the personality of Columbus, the adventurer, is very familiar as a result of the publicity which he arranged for himself. The discovery made him a famous man overnight, and his contemporaries have left us accounts of his single-mindedness, his somewhat pompous dignity, and his show-manship. Of his early life we only know what he himself had to say, and much of that is more creditable than credible. In a letter to Ferdinand and Isabella he recounts his former heroic exploits when he com-manded a ship sent to Tunis to capture the galley *Fernandina*, but the monarchs must have been aware of the fact that Columbus cannot have been much older than ten at that time.

According to this account, his crew was afraid of the superior enemy force, but he deceived them by fiddling with the compass. He later laid claim to a similar deception when he boasted that he had falsified the daily run of the *Santa Maria* on her great voyage of exploration. It is hardly surprising that a man who patently lied about his life history, and who actually prided himself on tricking the sailors who had entrusted their lives to his venture, turned out to be a disastrous administrator of the newly discovered islands. Indeed, he seemed to consider the New World as some sort of family possession, and in his absence delegated his power to his brothers Bartolomeo and Diego who equalled his incom-petence as rulers and surpassed him in cruelty. Finally the complaints of the colonists reached such a pitch that Ferdinand and Isabella had to appoint an investigator, Francisco Bobadilla, whom they sent out with full powers to try and establish law and order. On the strength of the charges and testimony before him he could have executed the Columbus brothers on the spot, but chose to send them to Spain instead. There Columbus appeared before the sovereigns who, in view of his services, decided to overlook all charges against him. They only suggested that, instead of being reinstated as Viceroy, he should be given a further com-mission of exploration. Thus in spite of the personal difficulties created by Columbus, and despite the fact that the new overseas possessions produced very little beyond tropical birds and disease, the sovereigns stood by him. There is little truth in the stories that he was badly treated and that his merit was not recognized.

Some historians have suggested that Columbus's lack of candour concerning his origin was due to the fact that he too was a Jew. In support of this they point out that the first American voyage was entirely financed by the Jews Luis Santangel and Isaac Abravanel. However, this is not a very cogent argument since the Jews in Spain were the progres-sive and enterprising element most willing to take financial risks, and thus were the obvious people to back any mercantile adventure. In addition, the rapidly increasing persecution of the Spanish Jews induced many to seek sanctuary in distant lands. Jews, in fact, as well as Moors, formed an appreciable proportion of the early settlers. On the other hand, the most reliable evidence suggests that Columbus was the son of a Genoese wool carder in modest circumstances, and that he first went to sea not as a navigator but as a wool trader. Since his first demand to Ferdinand and Isabella was for high-sounding titles such as 'Admiral' and 'Viceroy', and the right to call himself 'Don Cristobal', his reticence and lies about his youth were more likely due to the desire to hide his lowly birth than to any Jewish descent.

This, then, was the man who initiated one of the most important phases in the history of the white race. In view of these many instances of dishonesty, it has frequently been suggested that the idea of reaching the Indies by the western route had also been borrowed from somebody else, and a number of conjectures to this effect have been made. However, we have no concrete evidence of any kind to the effect that this was not Columbus's idea. The contrary is suggested by the existence of two letters, the authenticity of which is admittedly doubtful, sent by Paolo Toscanelli of Florence to Columbus in 1474. Toscanelli was a medical man who dabbled in geography, and who was particularly taken with Marco Polo's estimate of the overland distance between Europe and China. This estimate, like others of 'Messer Marco Millioni's', is on the generous side. Moreover, Toscanelli subscribed to the estimate, commonly accepted at that time, that the circumference of the earth was 18,000 miles. This value was based on the teaching of Posidonius (130–50 BC), who erroneously substituted this figure for the correct one of 25,000 miles, which had been experimentally deduced by Eratosthenes 150 years earlier. Toscanelli's overestimate of the extent of Asia, and his underestimate of the size of the earth, reduced the ocean gap between the west coast of Europe and East Asia from the actual 10,000 miles to half this amount. Columbus seems to have learned in Portugal of Toscanelli's theories, and to have written to him asking for details, and acquainting Toscanelli with his own idea of reaching India by the Atlantic route. Toscanelli's letters are in reply. The first was accompanied by a chart and, in the second, he comments on Columbus's plan '. . . that the voyage laid down is not only possible but certain, honourable, very advantageous and most glorious among all Christians'.

Columbus went from Genoa to Lisbon to follow his brother Bartolomeo, who had become a bookseller and cartographer, and had settled in the capital of ocean exploration. It was most likely through Bartolomeo that Columbus became interested in exploration, and his 'great idea' probably dates back to this contact. The Toscanelli letters date from the same time and it should be noted that, also in 1474, King Alfonso gave the Portuguese captain, Fernando Telles, the exclusive right to explore the Atlantic to the west. Thus, while we have no proof it seems quite likely that it was Columbus's own idea. Toscanelli appears to have accepted it as such, and Columbus could hardly have spied it out of the secret archives of the Portuguese research establishment for the simple reason that these contained the correct value of the earth's circumference. Most significant of all, however, is Columbus's tenacity in hanging onto his idea, which he regarded as a divine mission for which he had been chosen. Against all arguments, and to the exclusion of all other thought, he followed his plan.

Columbus's behaviour is typical of a man who, like the elder Cato, has one idea in his life with which he is so impressed that he repeats it over and over again. To a scientist this attitude will appear sterile and alien. Men like Newton, Einstein and Fermi all had dozens of ideas, all of which they worked on, and many of which they realized. It is rare that an inquiring mind will devote his whole lifetime to the pursuit of a single idea, and a man trained as a scientist would probably not hang onto it in the face of the well-documented criticism of his colleagues.

Columbus was no scientist. The discovery of America was a fluke, but a most significant one. With the Portuguese development of ocean navigation in the fifteenth century, the American continent was bound to be discovered at about that time. In fact, the Portuguese had evidently sent a number of secret expeditions into the Atlantic in search of the legendary island of Antilla, and may have found evidence of land. However, their scientists knew that the short sea route to India was around Africa and, quite rightly, they concentrated their main effort on its establishment.

Part of their scheme was to find the most favourable trade winds for the run to India. It was on a voyage planned and undertaken for this purpose that the Portuguese Pedro Alvarez Cabral, commanding a large merchant fleet bound for India via the Cape, sighted the South American coast in 1500. Thus, even if Columbus had never sailed, America would have been discovered within a decade. It is a feature of the scientific method that, once it sets out on a certain path in its often fumbling and seemingly haphazard manner, few things in this path are likely to remain undiscovered for long. Columbus's discovery of America was a fluke, but not an accident.

It may seem a pity that the Portuguese, who devoted all this superbly planned scientific effort to the exploration of the globe, should have

missed the prize of the American discovery. Most of Columbus's bio-
graphers dwell on the narrowness and lack of vision of the Portuguese
experts to whom King John II submitted, probably in 1483, Columbus's
plan to sail westward to India. But since the experts knew for certain
that this could not be done, they could hardly advise the King to support
the idea. And, in fact, their advice was sound. When Columbus died in
1506, the lands which he had discovered had yielded nothing in return
for the heavy sacrifice of men and ships but a few sticks of sugar cane
and some hunks of bacon. Spain was full of fever-stricken survivors who
had been fortunate enough to return alive from the islands which
Columbus had described to them as 'beautiful as the gardens of Valencia
in April'. They had lost their health, their comrades and their money in
that part of the world which, according to a curious geographical theory
of 'the Admiral', was a chosen region of the globe, a protuberance on
the otherwise round earth 'like a woman's nipple, this protrusion being
the highest and nearest the sky'.

At the same time, the wealth of the Orient trade was pouring into
Lisbon, whence it was trans-shipped to the harbours of Flanders, Germany and the Baltic. The sea route to the real Indies, the Indies of
spices, precious stones, ivory and silk, was rewarding Portugal for her
great scientific feat of exploration. The Indies of poor Columbus – and
to his dying day he was convinced that they were the real Indies – were
for a quarter of a century nothing but a horrible drain on the resources
of Spain. It was only the gold of Mexico and Peru which eventually
tipped the balance. Even though every schoolchild learns the name of
Columbus and the year 1492, they mean little in the history of white
domination. The Portuguese made the first step towards white supre-
macy by observation and mathematics, while Columbus tried to find
inspiration through interpretation of obscure passages in the Old
Testament. According to the Portuguese chronicler Barros, King John
II considered Columbus 'a big talker, and boastful in setting forth his
accomplishments, and full of fancy and imagination with his island of
Cypango, than certain whereof he spoke'. One suspects that King John's
judgment was not far off the mark.

It had been John II who, after the slow progress made during the
twenty years following the death of Henry the Navigator, had breathed
new life into the languishing overseas exploration programme. In his
vigorous exploration of the African coast, he established the stronghold
of Elmina on the Gulf of Guinea, which was to bring Portugal gold and
slaves. However, the ultimate prize, the sea route to India, eluded him.

On Bartolomeo Dias' return he named the Cape of Good Hope and knew that the way now lay open to his ships, but the final triumph of more than half a century of Portuguese exploration came only two years after his death in 1495. It fell to John's successor, Manuel, who became known as 'the Fortunate'. The king fitted out four ships, and placed them under the command of Vasco da Gama (who was born in the same year that Prince Henry had died). On 9 July the expedition sailed from Lisbon, after prayer and confession at the chapel of Santa Maria de Belem on the banks of the Tagus. Gama reached Calicut in the spring of the following year, and set up a marble column to mark the landfall in India.

The fact that the next expedition included no less than thirteen ships shows the confidence of the mariners in the mathematicians at the base. It was led by Cabral who, making use of the favourable trade winds, as we mentioned earlier, did not cling to the African coast but steered southwest into the Atlantic ocean. His aim, which he ultimately achieved, was to change course south of the equator, again making use of the trade winds to round the Cape of Good Hope. However, on 22 April 1500 Cabral sighted land to the west, which turned out to be the coast of Brazil. He immediately claimed it for the Portuguese crown. Since by the treaty of Tordesilla in 1494 Pope Alessandro Borgia had laid down that all land east of a meridian lying 370 leagues west of the Cape Verde Islands should belong to the Portuguese, Cabral's claim was justified. In fact it had not been disputed by the Spaniards when, a little earlier in 1500, one of their navigators, Vincente Pinzón, had sighted the same coast.

One wonders, incidentally, whether avoidance of the doldrums was the only reason for Cabral's extreme westerly course. While at present there is no proof that, in probing the Atlantic during the fifteenth century, the Portuguese had reached the American continent, this has often been suspected. We have to remember the extreme secretiveness of the Sagres establishment, and it may have been decided to delay the western exploration in order not to dissipate the main effort of pioneering the sea route to India. The close coincidence of Pinzón's and Cabral's voyages certainly gives food for thought. As we shall see, the Portuguese geographers knew a good deal more than they revealed.

On Vasco da Gama's triumphant return from India in 1499, King Manuel assumed the title 'Lord of the conquest, navigation and commerce of India, Ethiopia, Arabia and Persia'. He gave full credit to the new sciences, to which he owed his power, by adopting as his royal device the armillary sphere, the basic instrument of navigation. It shows the sphere of the heavens, divided by the polar and tropic circles and the equator, and crossed by the ecliptic, the sun's orbit. In its hollow centre stands the earth. The emblem also appears on the gold coins minted for use in India, and as an ornament of Manueline architecture in Lisbon and Coimbra. Another feature of this building style is the anchors and twisted ropes of his ships, which form the columns and surrounds of the monastery of Belem. Belem was founded in 1499, in commemoration of Vasco da Gama's voyage, and the explorer who had become Viceroy of India is buried there. It stands west of Lisbon, at a point on the bank of the Tagus where the explorers had set out on their voyage of discovery and conquest. In the river itself stands a fortified tower to protect the Portuguese ships from any attacker who might venture from the sea into the port.

After the death of Prince Henry, Belem had taken the place of both Sagres and Lagos. The lonely cliff jutting out into the Atlantic, with the little harbour at its foot, had been ideal in the early days of the project when the venture had been small enough to be kept completely secret. But with ever larger expeditions to be fitted out that remote location had become both unnecessary and inconvenient. Instead of a few navigators with small crews, ever increasing numbers of ships, men and supplies were needed, and what originally had been a clandestine operation was becoming a major national effort whose existence was abundantly obvious. The scholars, too, moved to Lisbon where they had the intellectual stimulus of the university, soon to be moved to Coimbra. Today the great heritage of the Portuguese exploration is perhaps best felt in this ancient university.

In the history of white domination, the universities of Europe were to play a key role. They gradually became the training centres for the practitioners of the new natural philosophy, although they had not been established for this purpose. In the late Middle Ages the monastic establishments of learning – the only ones that existed – had outlived their usefulness. Going beyond the narrow confines of religious studies, schools of medicine were established, such as the one at Salerno, and schools of law, of which Bologna and Paris were the main examples. The study of philosophy at these universities was the first sign heralding the advent of the Renaissance, and it was at Bologna that the young Copernicus conceived the idea of the heliocentric system.

But however closely the scholars of King Manuel's exploration may have been integrated with the Portuguese university, they still seem to

have kept their secrets. Their knowledge of the oceans and of distant
lands certainly far exceeded their published accounts. When examining
the original log of Vasco da Gama's voyage in the Municipal Library of
Oporto, I was shown a manuscript from the Holy Cross Monastery at
Coimbra. Called the *Chronicle of King D. Alfonso Henriques*, it is an
abstract of earlier documents prepared by Duarte Galvao at the request
of King Manuel. The most interesting part is the illuminated title-page,
which bears representations of the royal armillary sphere and a map of
the Portuguese world, reaching from Brazil in the west to the Malacca
Peninsula in the east. It is a remarkably accurate chart and it shows
unmistakably – the Antarctic continent.

When, 250 years later, Captain Cook searched for a southern continent, he crossed the south polar circle three times without sighting land,
and concluded in his report to the Admiralty that no such land mass
existed. It was not until 1820 that British, American and Russian
navigators finally established the existence of Antarctica. Close examination of the Portuguese *Chronicle* by Professor Antonio Cruz shows that
it dates from the early sixteenth century. With this astonishing insight
into the secret working of the Portuguese scientific establishment, one
wonders whether Columbus's discovery of America in 1492 may not in
fact have been forestalled by the Portuguese.

The first chapter in the story of white domination, the discovery of
the earth, took the Portuguese less than a century, but it changed the
face of the world completely. However, they were not destined to reap
the fruit of their labours. King Manuel was, after all, not very fortunate.
He had dreamt of ruling the globe by gaining, in addition to his own
possessions, those of Spain as well. He had thought to achieve his aim by
marrying the Spanish heiress, the eldest daughter of Ferdinand and
Isabella. However, his queen died giving birth to the much desired heir,
who shortly followed her into the grave. In the end it was the king of
Spain, Philip II, who combined the two kingdoms and for ever dashed
Portuguese aspirations of becoming the foremost world power. His
bigoted intolerance drove out the scholars, who fled to the Low Countries and England where they continued their work and set up new and
active schools.

CHAPTER THREE

Divine beauty of simplicity

Thus, at the beginning of the sixteenth century, European man not only knew that the earth was round but, thanks to the ingenuity of the Jews in Portugal, he was also able to find his way about it. Less than a hundred years earlier the problem of ocean navigation had not even been posed, and the roundness of the earth was an item of information about as useful as the number of angels able to dance on the point of a needle. The accepted value for the latter was, I think, forty, and the process of logical deduction by which it was arrived at was probably more complex than that leading to the spherical nature of the earth. The great change which had taken place in those hundred years was simply that information concerning the globe had become extremely valuable, whereas the dancing angels had remained exactly as useless as they had been before.

We have no reason to believe that the Renaissance brought a change in the way men's minds work when they are confronted with a problem requiring logical deduction. Only the emphasis had changed. Far from being an obstacle to the mastery of the forces of nature, the scholastic training of the Middle Ages was a valuable preparation for the tasks ahead. The ability to perform intricate logical exercises can be transferred easily from one subject to another, completely unrelated to the first. A typical example is that of the Ashkenase Jews during the last century after their emancipation from the ghettos of Europe. Forced into intellectual isolation by religious intolerance, they had devoted themselves for centuries to the narrow and sterile interpretation of their sacred literature. Since no addition to this had been made for a thousand years, any new conclusions had to employ complex chains of logical deduction, and a vast amount of reference to earlier authorities. This type of intensive training proved eminently successful in a great diversity of professions which the Jews entered after emancipation, and the pursuit of modern science, especially theoretical physics, is clearly one of them. The great contributions made by the Sephardic Jews 400 years earlier may have been due to a similar utilization of previous training. And at the present time we are witnessing outstanding successes in theoretical physics by Chinese and Japanese scholars. Again, in both these countries there exists a long history of strict mental discipline in intellectual activities requiring great power of sustained concentration. Anyone who can master the intricacies of Chinese literature, with its allusions and complex cross-references, has probably the necessary equipment for battling with the problems of modern science.

It therefore would seem that the issue of the dancing angels is not nearly as ridiculous as we are inclined to think. Its solution was a fine piece of mental acrobatics, and the type of man capable of doing this would have the right training to prove that the heavens are not a crystal sphere surrounding our earth, but of immense extent. And indeed, the first great step towards modern science taken by a single individual was made by a son of the Church, with a sound university training in Canon Law. Nicholas Copernicus was still a child of the Middle Ages in both his life and his thought. The path he walked was the same as that of many generations of churchmen before him. He was no innovator in outlook but, as if in a compelling trance, he put an entirely new emphasis on the result of his labours. Thus the lonely old man at the Baltic coast became a trail-blazer of the new age.

As everybody knows, Copernicus took the earth out of the centre of the universe and put the sun into its place. Except that Copernicus himself, true to his nature, learned and correct, modestly quotes 'Philolaus the Pythagorean, a remarkable mathematician' as having had the same idea nearly two thousand years earlier. As usual, the Greeks had been there before with the correct interpretation as well as with all the incorrect ones. And, as with the size of the globe, they fastened eventually on the wrong one for the solar system. It made no difference either to them or to those who followed until suddenly, at about AD 1500, man began to look at the heavens with new eyes.

Astronomy is probably the oldest of the sciences. The question of time and the thought of periodicity, as day follows day and year follows year, must have been among the earliest concepts formed in the human mind. The great monuments of our distant past, the pyramids of Egypt and the stone circles of Northern Europe, are geared to the movement of the stars and the sun. The sun and the stars would tell man how much longer his hoarded food had to be stretched through the winter, when it was time to sow again, and when he could expect the next inundation

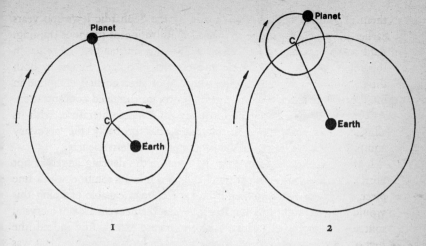

Figs. 4, 5. The Greeks believed that the planets move in perfectly circular orbits around a centre 'C' which itself circles the earth. With these combinations of excentric (1) and epicycle (2), Ptolemy was able to acocunt for the observed paths of the planets in the sky with remarkable accuracy.

of the Nile. They were the great eternal clock, the calendar, and this they remained until Copernicus gave them an entirely new significance.

The Greeks had speculated upon the nature of the heavenly clock but, since they were only interested in keeping the right time, its true mechanism was of little importance to them. Thus although Philolaus had hit on the correct model in 300 B C, his successors of the Alexandrian school preferred one with the earth at its centre, since it appeared to them more natural, and provided all the information which was required. This was handed on to Western man in Ptolemy's *Amalgest*, which formed the basis of all astronomical teaching in the late Middle Ages.

The heavens, with the sun, the moon, the planets and the stars, appear to turn around us in twenty-four hours, but this observation provides no more than the notion of day and night. Knowledge of the seasons, and the forecast of their duration, has to be obtained from the much slower motion of the planets, seen against the background of the 'fixed' stars. Sun, moon and planets each carry out individual movements against this background, which led to the idea that they were attached to separate transparent crystal spheres, all turning inside each other like a set of Chinese ivory balls. The sphere of the stars was held to be furthest, and the sphere carrying the moon to be closest to the earth. The apparent motion of these objects in the sky takes place roughly along the same circle, the Zodiac, but is by no means absolutely regular. The planets, especially, describe complicated orbits, going forward in their paths most of the time, but then moving backward again for a while.

Ptolemy was able to account for all this in a very satisfactory manner, with a theory which followed the conventional pattern of Greek thought. The sun and moon were perfect spheres, and could be expected to move in perfect orbits which therefore must be circles. The retrograde motion of the planets made it clear that their orbits could not be described by circles about a common centre, and so the mathematical device of epicycles was introduced. If the axle of a little wheel is fastened to the rim of a large wheel, and both wheels are rotating, a point on the rim of the little wheel moves in an epicycle. Thus to an observer stationed at the axle of the big wheel, this point will sometimes appear to move with it and sometimes to go backwards. Such a composite motion, when applied to the heavenly bodies, fitted in reasonably well with the observations, and at the same time accorded with the philosophical concept of perfect circles. In order to account for the slight deviation of the observed motion of the planets from the calculated epicycles, the Greeks made the additional assumption that the earth did not stand exactly in the centre of the planetary orbits. By combining this 'excentric' with the epicycles, they were able to describe and predict the motion of the heavenly bodies with remarkable accuracy. In fact, for anyone regarding the heavens solely as a calendar, Ptolemy's earth-centred system does all that is needed, with no alternative or innovation required. A man who can see a clock-tower with a reliable timepiece from his window does not have to know anything about the mechanism of that particular clock in order to know the time.

With the Portuguese voyages the stars acquired a new significance. They became the means by which the navigators found their way on the round earth. Columbus noted that the true north indicated by the stars differed from that shown by his compass. Bartolomeo Dias, as he approached the Antarctic pole of the earth, was the first European to see the unknown constellations of the southern sky rise above the horizon. To the men of this age the heavens had ceased to be a mere clock, and they began to sense that some relation should exist between their own

12, 13 Navigational techniques at the beginning of the ocean-going era. Diagrams explaining the use of the Jacob's Staff (*left*) and determination of latitude with an astrolabe (*right*) appeared in the manual *Regimiento de navegacion*, 1563.

14, 15 Examples of early navigational aids. *Left*, a ship's compass dating from 1580. *Below*, a Jacob's Staff on the left, in the centre a backstaff, and a mariner's astrolabe on the right.

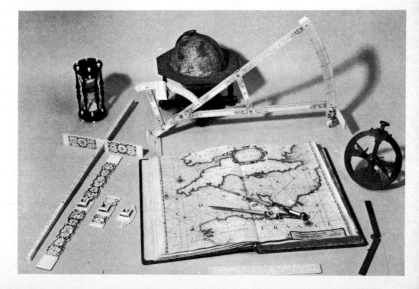

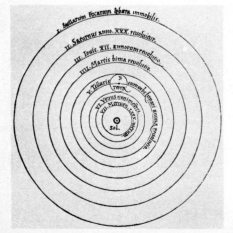

16, 17 *Top left*, Nicholas Copernicus (1473–15.
whose conception of the 'beauty of simplicity'
and is—fundamental to the development of na
science. *Above*, the Jagiellonian University in
Cracow where Copernicus studied.

18, 19 *Left*, the title-page of Copernicus's *De
Revolutionibus*, which was not published till the
year of his life, with (*below, left*) a woodcut fro
the book illustrating the heliocentric system. *B*
the Copernican theory was extended by Thom
Digges (d. 1595), according to whom the stars
no longer fixed on a crystal sphere but scattere
through the universe.

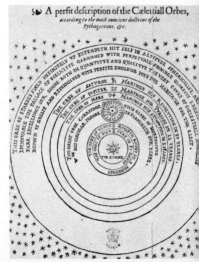

20, 21, 22 *Above*, Tycho Brahe (1546–1601), with the silver nose which he designed after losing his own in a duel. Uraniborg (*below*), Brahe's observatory on the isle of Hveen, was granted to him by King Frederick II of Denmark. It contained the great mural quadrant (*right*), where his accurate observation of planetary motion provided the basis for the work of Kepler and Newton.

ORTHOGRAPHIA PRÆCIPVÆ DOMVS ARCIS VRANIBVRGI
in Infula Porthmi Danici Venufia, *vulgo* Huenna, Aftronomiæ inftaurandæ gratia, circa annum MDLXXX,
à TYCHONE BRAHE exædificatæ.

25 Two early telescopes, probably made by Galileo himself.

23, 24 *Above*, Johannes Kepler (1571–1630), Tycho's colleague and successor as Imperial Mathematician to the Habsburg Emperor Rudolph II. Kepler was a brilliant mathematician but did not as yet make a clear distinction between astronomy and astrology. *Below*, his attempt to explain the size of planetary orbits by means of a geometrical model.

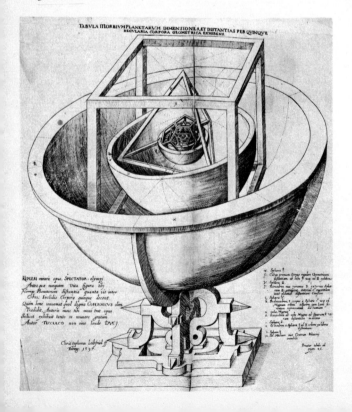

globe and the heavenly bodies. Already quite a number of people were beginning to suspect that it was not the dome of the heavens which was spinning around the earth each twenty-four hours, but that the earth was turning on its own axis. Its spherical shape and the symmetry of the two poles, which now had become established fact, made this idea more acceptable than it would have been a hundred years before.

These new thoughts ring through the opening chapters of Copernicus's great book, *On the Revolutions of the Heavenly Spheres*, when he talks about the recent discovery of America, and the certainty that the inhabitants of that continent must be antipodal to those living on the banks of the Ganges. The globe of the earth suspended in space is a reality to him, revealed by exploration carried out in his lifetime, and not just a philosophical argument. His system, with the sun in the centre and the earth nothing but another planet, is much more than a clock or a calendar. In one magnificent stroke he abolished the complex Greek epicycles by explaining that the observed retrograde motion of the planets is only apparent, and due to the motion of the earth around the sun. The beauty of this new system is simplicity and, as he states in his dedication to the Pope, God is revealed in this beauty of His work. The reader is made to feel that this great vision, the first glimpse of a universal pattern of the physical world, must have come to Copernicus in his youth. From that moment his life was dedicated to its proof and confirmation.

We have the manuscript of his book, the first printed copy of which he saw on the day he lay dying. It bears the evidence of constant correction and improvement, of striving for perfection in comprehending the divine pattern. He lost much time in trying to prove his system on the basis of observations recorded in the *Amalgest*, which had been made 1500 years earlier and were often faulty. Like his contemporaries, he trusted the wisdom of the Greeks with the same undoubting faith which he had in the scriptures. Glaring inconsistencies finally drove him to making observations of his own, most of which were undertaken in later life. Even so, he remained essentially a mathematician, and the instruments which he had made for his work were simple and not very accurate.

This should not be taken to mean that the work of Copernicus is merely a continuation of the speculations advanced in antiquity. His criteria for a true description of planetary motion were simplicity and universality, and he had no other justification for choosing them than his belief that the works of God are revealed to us in this way. And now, after four centuries packed with scientific development, we still have no other justification for our way of thinking. The great pioneers of modern science, such as Maxwell, Planck and Einstein, have often been deeply religious men, because they have felt that this beauty of simplicity experienced by the human mind reveals a divine creation of the universe in which man himself is an integral part. In science the age-old idea that man must be in harmony with the surrounding world has found a new and deeper significance. The domination of the forces of nature achieved by the white race is based on the firm belief that the most general interpretation which can explain a wide variety of natural phenomena must be correct. Far from losing itself in the apparent complexity of new discoveries, the aim of basic science is to find the underlying pattern which, we are certain, must be simple.

It was the beauty of simplicity of his solar system which convinced Copernicus, not its superior strength in calculating planetary motion. In fact, Copernicus never saw the improvement in astronomical prediction which his system permitted. In 1514, when he was called to Rome to take part in a reform of the calendar, he declined the invitation on the grounds that much further observation was required before such a task could be undertaken. Paucity of data hampered his work, and he was loath to present it to the world in an imperfect form. When he was about forty he wrote up an abstract of his ideas in the famous *Commentariolus* (*Little Commentary*) which he sent in manuscript form to some of his friends. It contains a full summary of his ideas, but no proof or support. These were reserved for a book to be published later, for which he waited another thirty years. But it is significant that one of the observations recorded in it was made by Copernicus in Bologna when he was twenty-four, which suggests that the idea of the heliocentric system must have come to him there.

Unlike the Portuguese cartographers, and unlike most of his successors, Copernicus was never a professional scientist. Born in 1473 in Torun on the Vistula, the son of Nicholas Koppernick, a merchant, young Nicholas was educated by his maternal uncle, Lucas Waczelrodt. The father had died when Nicholas was still small, and uncle Lucas, a forceful personality who became bishop of Ermland, arranged for his nephew to follow in his own footsteps. This meant, first, the Jagiellonian University of Cracow where the record of his entry is still preserved, as a result of which the Poles have claimed him as their greatest son. However, four years later he entered the German fraternity at the University of Bologna, spelling his name 'Kopperlingk', and this has in the course of the centuries transformed him into an outstanding *German* astronomer. Copernicus himself would have been at a loss to solve the riddle; he was a citizen of the late medieval world, a priest owing obedience to the Pope in Rome, and he wrote – and presumably thought – in Latin. His studies were those of an *uomo universale*. Besides taking a doctorate in Canon Law he read philosophy, mathematics, astronomy, Greek and medicine, and he practised in all these subjects. He translated some late Greek poems of pastoral and amorous content into Latin, and dedicated the volume to his uncle the bishop, whom he also attended as physician. In addition he acted as his uncle's secretary in the acrimonious disputes between the King of Poland and the Grand Master of the Teutonic Knights, wrote a treatise on the reform of the currency, and administered the territories belonging to his chapter. One begins to suspect that, like some other great scientific ideas, the Copernican system owes its existence to the escapist tendencies of the originator. It seems that, in the intervals between wars, political intrigues, illness in high places and financial operations, Copernicus relaxed in the company of his planetary computations. Moreover, they were the link with his youth, with Cracow, Bologna, Padua, Ferrara and Rome.

When young Nicholas was twenty-four, his uncle Waczelrodt had him appointed canon at Frauenburg on the Baltic coast, an office which he held until his death at seventy. It was the ideal thing. The duties were not arduous, and in any case Copernicus did not come into residence for another fifteen years, until after the death of his uncle. Together with a Silesian prebend, his office at Frauenburg provided Copernicus with an adequate income, a place to live and a good social status. The canons lived the life of noblemen, they were entitled to carry arms, and the vow of celibacy did not weigh too heavily on them. Evidently Lucas Waczelrodt had hoped to make young Nicholas into a bishop, but the latter seems to have preferred a quiet life with time for his astronomical studies to the limelight of an exalted position. A secure existence, unostentatious enough to allow for a certain degree of home comfort, was the life which Nicholas Copernicus had chosen for himself. The man who furnished the basic pattern of modern scientific thought was a leisured scholar, not a revolutionary.

As we have seen, the great vision had come to him as a student when he was Novara's pupil in Bologna, and he had perceived that scientific truth is revealed in simplicity. One can well imagine what happened next. He fitted the existing observations into a system with the sun at its centre and, lo and behold, it worked out correctly. Now more and more accurate data were needed to present the miracle of beauty to the world. For a while things went well, but then troubles began to crop up. No doubt, Copernicus had hoped for perfect planetary circles with the sun as centre, but this was not to be. He too had to make use of epicycles and excentrics. Admittedly they were much smaller than those of Ptolemy, and the speed of the planets was uniform in them, but nevertheless it was strange and disconcerting that God had not chosen the simplest pattern. Copernicus must have been assailed by terrible doubts in his vision of simplicity, but its beauty, even in imperfect form, was too great to be discarded. We now understand why he did not journey to Rome to reform the calendar, and why he was reluctant to publish his book. Something was wrong and he must have hoped to find it. As his life was drawing to its close the hope faded.

Then, as if sent by fate, a prophet appeared. Four years before the old man's death a young professor from the Lutheran University of Wittenberg suddenly turned up in Frauenburg. Georg Joachim von Lauchen, who called himself Rheticus, was born when Copernicus sent out his *Commentariolus*. It had taken twenty-five years to bear fruit. The pupil, the only one Copernicus ever had, persuaded him to publish his great book without waiting for further inspiration. Three years earlier Cardinal Schoenberg of Capua, too, had written to Copernicus, begging him to communicate his discovery to the world and offering at the same time to have a copy made at his own expense. Copernicus had done nothing. The Cardinal was a man of much greater influence than Rheticus, but he was far away whereas Rheticus was now on the spot. He succeeded where the Cardinal had failed. The final touches were applied to the manuscript, computations were checked, and in two years it was ready for the press. After another two years the Canon's dying hands were resting on the first printed copy. His great vision, received almost half a century earlier, was now before the world, its beauty almost complete. Only Copernicus knew that there was a flaw somewhere, and fifty years of labour had not succeeded in detecting it. The planetary orbits were simple, but they were not nearly simple enough.

The correct explanation did not merely require a new revelation, it also required a new type of man: the observer and experimentalist. If a miracle had provided Copernicus with the ultimate solution of the planetary orbits, it would have helped him little. The observational data at his disposal were quite inadequate to prove it. Tycho Brahe had to come, a man who did not believe in the Copernican system but who furnished all the observations which were needed for its final triumph. Armed with Tycho's life work, as well as dogged determination and the enthusiasm of a fanatic, another mathematical genius had to appear on the scene to make Copernicus's vision of truth become reality. A century after Copernicus made his first observations, Johannes Kepler 'stumbled by chance' on the solution of the planetary orbits. This is the phrase he used, but it was not accidental stumbling; it was a slow and determined effort to fit a curve to the observed positions of the planet Mars. There are no 'accidents' in science, and Kepler's work is an ideal example of this. When finally he had the correct solution, he did not realize it because he had made an error in his computation. Only some time later, when he approached the same mathematical problem in a different way, did he understand what had happened. He had been at his goal but had failed to recognize it. If he had failed for a second time to perceive the truth, or even for a third or a fourth time, he would still have gone on until he had attained it. There are no accidents in science; the solution may be delayed a little, or it may be reached by a lucky throw a little ahead of time, but only a little.

That was the end of the laboured circles with epicycles and excentrics. Copernicus's belief that the work of God is revealed in simplicity was true. The orbits of Mars and of all the other planets turned out to be ellipses, beautiful, perfect ellipses, with the sun in one of the focal points. Nothing could be more simple and satisfying. Only, by then the vision which God had granted to Copernicus had become a dangerous belief from which Giordano Bruno had to be cleansed at the stake.

The execution of Bruno, who incidentally persisted in quite a number of other heresies as well, and the trial of Galileo, have often been used as arguments that Copernicus hesitated to publish his book for fear of persecution. There is not a shred of evidence for this. On the contrary, the Church was in favour of his work. He dedicated his book to Pope Paul III, and Cardinal Schoenberg had besought him to publish it. We also know that the predecessors of Paul III showed the most benevolent interest in the Copernican theory. The private secretaries of both Leo X and Clement VII lectured before these popes and their learned friends on the new system of the world proposed by the canon in Frauenburg, and we are told that in each case these lectures were well received. Indeed, here was a scholarly son of the Church of whom Rome could be proud, while the attackers were in the Protestant camp.

On 31 October 1517 Martin Luther had nailed his 95 theses on the church door at Wittenberg, and within a few years the Reformation had spread throughout the length and breadth of Germany. The scorn and fury of the reformers turned mainly against the corruption of the priests, and Luther found that his vehement and often obscene language brought him enthusiastic followers among the common people. The priests were an easy target, and Luther had no need to enter upon the profound import of the Copernican theory in order to jeer at its author as 'that new astrologer who wants to prove that the Earth goes round the sun' and to denounce him as 'a fool who goes against Holy Writ'. Luther knew what language and arguments please the masses, and as a result of his jibes Copernicus was caricatured in a carnival parade at Elbing, not far from Frauenburg. In a more sophisticated vein the theoretician of the Reformation, Philip Melanchthon, supposedly refuted the Copernican system; and another high ranking member of the Lutheran party, Osiander, tried his best to turn Copernicus's vision into a mathematical parlour trick. Rheticus, without whom the book of the revolutions would never have been published, was a Protestant. After great difficulties he finally succeeded in getting the book printed in Nuremberg, but before it was finished he had to leave for a new post as professor in Leipzig. He handed the task on to his famous co-religionist in Nuremberg, Andreas Osiander, who promptly seized the opportunity of inserting an unsigned preface of his own which stated that the hypotheses advanced in the book were unlikely to be true or even probable, that they were full of absurdities, and that the only reason for advancing them was their use as a calculating aid. In other words, here was a clever method for calendar computations, but one without any deeper significance. The insidious feature of Osiander's preface was that the reader was led to believe it was written by the author of the book and, in fact, its true authorship was only discovered by Kepler in the following century. The contention that it was Osiander's aim to protect the book from persecution by the Church is not very convincing. The Church was approving and, moreover, Osiander was a Lutheran. It is more likely that in this underhand way Osiander tried to please Luther and Melanchthon, whom he knew to be opposed to the Copernican system. All this happened during the last few months of Copernicus's life, and it is not even certain whether he ever saw the substituted preface or whether, as is sometimes asserted, it hastened his end.

During Copernicus's lifetime the Counter Reformation had not yet got under way, and nobody had as yet conceived the idea that the heliocentric system was a mortal danger to the Catholic Church. If Copernicus had his difficulties with the ecclesiastical authorities, it was not on account of his theory. The Lutherans lashed at the corrupt priests who lived openly with women, and the Church became sensitive about standards of morality among the clergy. Copernicus was very much a child of his age. At the time when he studied in Italy the Holy See was occupied by Pope Alexander VI, Borgia, whose son Cesare and daughter Lucrezia were universally known. It seems that later in Frauenberg Copernicus followed the example of other members of the cathedral chapter in keeping a *focaria*, which term denotes a housekeeper in the widest sense of the word. It appears that in 1538, when the pressure of the Reformation had become strong, the new bishop of Ermland, Dantiscus, must have made some remarks enjoining greater circumspection in these matters, and it appears equally clear that Copernicus must have lent a deaf ear to this. The bishop, too, was a child of the same age, and a man of the world who not only had a beautiful daughter, Dantisca, born to him by Ysope de Galda of Toledo, but had also dedicated an elegant poem to another lady in Innsbruck. Since letters only appear late in the exchange of views between the bishop and the canon concerning Anna Schilling, the latter's housekeeper, we may assume that Dantiscus, who regarded Copernicus highly, restricted himself at first to verbal hints. Even when he had to become more insistent, he tactfully approached another bishop, Tiedemann Giese, Copernicus's closest friend, rather than writing to the canon personally. Copernicus prevaricated over sending away Anna as much as over the publication of his book and, either in great innocence or with sly humour, he headed his letter to Dantiscus with the Greek translation of Frauenburg – Gynopoly – the City of Women. Yes, he did send her away but, it appears from the report of another canon, only to meet her from now on in town. He was then sixty-six, and a letter written by the bishop to Giese suggests that the reason for interference in the astronomer's private affairs was a fear that the old man would get into trouble with the authorities of the Church.

At the age of seventy Copernicus died peacefully in his tower in Frauenburg, the first true scientist of our age, the discoverer of the touchstone of simplicity, the founder of a new philosophy. He was a scholar whose life evidently passed without great conflicts, a man who had the same virtues and weaknesses as many of us. He is remembered for the system which bears his name, but his contribution to man's knowledge reached far beyond the solar system.

In addition to the concept of the heliocentric solar system Copernicus also provided our civilization with the proof of a large universe. This second new idea he did not introduce as an independent postulate, but because he needed it in order to make his solar system acceptable. Since Aristotle it had been taken for granted that the outermost of the celestial crystal spheres surrounding the earth was the one carrying the fixed stars. The first and obvious argument to be raised against the Copernican system was that the apparent distance between individual stars did not change in the course of a year. If, it was said, the earth was swinging around the sun like a child on a roundabout, we would be near some of the stars now and far away from them six months later. Like by-standers near the roundabout, the constellations would appear large to the rider when near and small when he was at the opposite side of our circuit. Since it was well known that the observed distances between individual stars in the constellations never changed, there was only one way of saving the heliocentric system: the sphere of the fixed stars must be very large in comparison with the earth and its orbit. A distant church spire will not appear larger or smaller to us from either side of the roundabout.

Copernicus removed this difficulty in the first chapter of his book in order to clear the decks for his solar system. He did this elegantly and decisively, by a simple geometrical proof. Suppose that a star A is rising in the east, while another star B is setting in the west; when A in turn is setting in the west, B should still be well below the eastern horizon if the earth and the celestial sphere are of comparable size. The observed fact that when A sets, B rises again – after exactly twelve hours – proves that the earth is infinitesimally small when compared to the distance of the stars.

For Copernicus the immediate use of this elegant proof was that it enabled him to get on with the heliocentric mechanism, and we do not know whether he gave thought again to the enormous universe which he had created. He continued to speak of the sphere of the fixed stars, possibly because his training in Canon Law had taught him not to com-plicate his main argument by introducing side issues. That his proof of the immensity of the heavens had done away with the concept of a universe limited by a crystal sphere is clearly shown in a book which the English astronomer Thomas Digges published thirty-four years later. It shows the solar system still surrounded by a sphere, but the stars are now beyond it, scattered far away at different distances from the sun.

Neither was there any point now in keeping the sun at the centre of the universe. This had already been shown earlier by the German Cardinal, Nicholas of Cusa, who, when speculating on an infinite

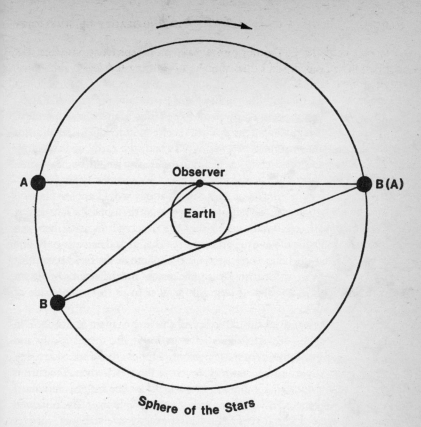

Fig. 6. The Greeks assumed that the stars are fixed upon a celestial sphere. Copernicus provided an elegant proof that this sphere must be very large compared to the size of the earth. Otherwise, for an observer who sees a star (A) rising at the same time as another star (B) is setting, B would still be below the horizon when A, in turn, is setting. But this, as he showed, is not the case.

universe, had pointed out that the earth would be at the same time on its periphery and in its centre. At the time this was nothing but a piece of late medieval scholasticism. However, it now came in useful. The next, and great, step forward took place when in 1609 Galileo turned the newly invented telescope towards the sky.

Just as the ocean-going ships of the Portuguese had opened the globe for exploration, so the telescope opened up the heavens. In this newly created natural philosophy of the Renaissance, speculation became increasingly based on observation, and for this reason the tools of observa-

tion acquired a special significance. The age of instruments became an
integral part of the scientific method, and the invention of new and
powerful instruments became as essential for the exploitation of natural
resources as the method itself. From now on all progress was based on
instrumental observation. Only by the creation of new instruments was
the West able to open up new worlds, and thus gain the ascendancy
over others who had remained in the old one.

The invention of the first of these powerful instruments is shrouded
in mystery. Legend has it that the children of a Dutch spectacle-maker
were playing with old lenses and, through the lucky combination of
two of them, saw the distant church tower of Middelburg greatly
magnified. The story is repeated here not because it is likely to be true
but because it is significant, and because it has been re-enacted again and
again in the history of science. At the end of the sixteenth century people
had learned to grind lenses, and this means that the telescope and
microscope were due for invention. Who actually invented them is
neither certain nor terribly important. Many of our instruments and
devices have several inventors, most of whom are quite genuine. The
ultimate choice for the awarding of the palm thus depends largely on
luck, national pride, publicity and other fortuitous circumstances. In any
case, lenses began to be combined into telescopes – without anyone
understanding fully the underlying principle – and in the first decade of
the seventeenth century Galileo built one and looked through it into
the sky.

On the night of 7 January 1609 he directed his telescope at Jupiter and
saw, close to the planet, three little stars. Three nights later he noticed
that they had changed position, and after another three nights he saw a
fourth star. Galileo immediately grasped the significance of his observation, and realized that he had discovered satellites of Jupiter which
circle around the planet as our moon does around the earth. He saw in
it a proof for the Copernican system which was further strengthened
when, a few months later, he observed that the planet Venus shows
phases like the moon. Looking at the moon through the telescope, he
discovered that its surface is not smooth but as full of mountains as that
of the earth. He published his discoveries in his first book, the *Sidereus
Nuncius* (*Star Messenger*), which spread his fame but met with a good
deal of incredulity. Much of the latter may have been due to the factual
style, which avoided all circumlocution, and which his contemporaries
considered boastful. Galileo's true feelings, however, are clearly expressed in a letter to the Duke of Tuscany in which he says: 'I am full of

infinite astonishment and also of infinite gratitude to God that it has pleased Him to make me alone the first observer of such wonderful things that in all the past centuries remained hidden.' Written at the beginning of Western science, these words describe admirably the sense of humility and exultation which follows a discovery. The everyday world with its human passions and miseries recedes before a revelation of truth which has the power of a religious experience.

Strictly speaking, none of Galileo's discoveries constitutes a rigorous proof that the earth rotates round the sun, but all his observations were in good agreement with the Copernican system, and difficult to understand on the basis of the old ideas. This is a state of affairs frequently encountered in the history of scientific thought when, in the absence of irrefutable proof, the existing body of evidence has to be weighed in favour of or against a particular set of concepts. With the spread of exploration and the growth of observational material, discrepancies are bound to arise all the time, and it is often difficult to decide at what stage these discrepancies have become strong enough to require the discarding of a conceptual framework which has proved useful in the past.

Another of Galileo's early observations – also mentioned in the *Sidereus Nuncius* – had, in the long run, a more far-reaching effect than those mentioned above. He noted that, unlike the planets, the stars did not appear as discs in the telescope but remained points, and also that the telescope revealed a far greater number of stars than had been visible to the naked eye. In particular, he pointed out that the Milky Way was dissolved by the telescope into a multitude of faint stars.

Copernicus had not altered the concept of a 'sphere of the stars' but, as we have seen, he had to prove that this sphere must be very large in order to make the heliocentric solar system acceptable. Neither had he disagreed with the common belief that the stars, like the planets, shine by virtue of light reflected from the sun. It is clearly difficult to explain how the stars can be very far away from the sun and nevertheless brightly reflect its light. If Copernicus noticed this discrepancy, and one would suspect that it must have occurred to him, he did not say anything about it. His foremost interest was in the solar system, and here it was bad enough that the planetary orbits were not perfect circles.

Copernicus became the trail-blazer of Western science, not so much because his heliocentric system proved to be correct, but because he proposed it. As we have seen, the Ptolemaic system was good enough to provide all the necessary data for establishing and checking the calendar, and thus all the information needed by the farmer and men in general. In fact it was somewhat superior to the Copernican system in its original state, and nobody knew this better than Copernicus himself who, for this reason, had declined to go to Rome for a reformation of the calendar.

However, whereas man in the Middle Ages accepted the movement of the planets as ordained by God's unfathomable wisdom, Copernicus looked for the *reason* in God's wisdom. While accepting it, he wanted to know why the Almighty had made the planets move in just this particular way. In other words, he was looking for the theory which God had used. Scientists know that it is usually more difficult to ask the right question than to give the correct answer. Copernicus's question constitutes the fundamental intellectual step out of the Middle Ages into the modern world. His heliocentric system did not bring any material advantage to mankind but, by raising the question of its meaning, it opened an entirely new way of thinking which made possible the material progress leading to white domination. His dissatisfaction with the Ptolemaic system was not due to its lack of accuracy, but because he could see no reason behind it. He was groping for an understanding of the law which he felt God must have given to the motion of the heavenly bodies.

The divine law upon which he hit for an explanation was the beauty of simplicity which, as it turned out, was not the true reason for the planets circling the sun. The fact that they almost, but not quite, circled it confused and dismayed Copernicus so much that, but for Rheticus's intervention, his book would probably never have been published. After his death more than a century had to elapse before Isaac Newton found the correct law: the theory of gravitation. It provided the answer to the question which the young Copernicus had asked, and this answer was ultimately to provide the intellectual impetus for the rapid scientific and technological advance of the West. However, it was Copernicus who had asked the right question.

Newton, on the other hand, could not have formulated his theory on the legacy which Copernicus left. Before the laws of celestial mechanics could be discovered, two important steps had to be taken after Copernicus. Accurate observations of the planetary motions had to be made, and then these observations had to be expressed in mathematical form. The two men who were to provide the bridge between Copernicus and Newton, Tycho Brahe and Kepler, were not yet born when Copernicus died. Tycho, who performed the first task, was by nature an observer and not a theoretician. As we have seen, he did not even believe in the Copernican system, but substituted for it a model of his own in which the earth stayed motionless in the centre around which the sun, with the planets circling it, rotated. All that can be said about Tycho's system is that it combined the drawbacks of both the Ptolemaic and the Copernican model, confusing rather than giving help to theoretical interpretation.

In a way Tycho was more akin to the Portuguese explorers than to Copernicus; he was a practitioner rather than a philosopher. As the Portuguese scholars charted the globe, Tycho charted the heavens. Barely on the threshold of the new age, he was a swashbuckling nobleman who had his nose cut off in a duel, and then had recourse to the scientific expedient of having it replaced by a silver one – a course of action which well illustrated his attitude to life. Born in Knudstrup in Denmark, he fell out with his family over his marriage to a peasant girl. But after travelling widely in the course of his studies, he was eventually offered the use of his uncle's castle at Knudstrup to set up an observatory. This was the beginning of his career as an astronomer, which was established after one year, in 1572, by the observation of a new star. His publication of the event went against the clerical idea that the heavens were eternal and unchanging, but seems to have resulted in credit rather than disadvantage. King Frederick II of Denmark, at least, was so impressed with the young nobleman that he bestowed on him a life pension, a canonry, the income of an estate in Norway, and the island of Hveen, where Tycho set up his famous observatory of Uraniborg. Here he installed a number of large astronomic instruments with which, for more than twenty years, he carried out the systematic astronomical observations that formed the basis of all subsequent developments in this field. He just did not live to see the invention of the telescope, which would have increased immeasurably the breadth of his work. As it was, Tycho listed, in addition to his observations on planets and comets, the accurate position of no less than 777 stars.

In the end Tycho's medieval attitude proved his undoing. His arrogant treatment of the peasants of Hveen caused the next king to revoke his pension and fief, and the astronomer now moved to Prague to become the court astrologer and mathematician of Emperor Rudolph II. True to form and in accordance with his status, Tycho was given the castle of Benatky near the capital, and his instruments were moved there from Denmark in 1599. There he lived in style with his family and retinue of servants and co-workers, foremost among whom was another nobleman astronomer, the Junker Franz Tengnagel von Camp, who had married one of Tycho's daughters. At Benatky Tycho was joined, one year after his arrival, by an impecunious young Protestant from Germany: Johannes Kepler.

Kepler, too, possibly even more than Copernicus and Tycho, was a child of the Middle Ages. His mother had been accused of being a witch and, although she was eventually rescued from conviction by the intervention of her illustrious son, probably was one. Her magic potions had miraculously cured, and occasionally poisoned, her neighbours and their livestock, and she had been prevented with some difficulty from exhuming her father, whose cranium she wished to turn into a drinking-bowl. Kepler himself probably regarded the horoscopes which he cast for the Emperor and the famous Count Wallenstein as more than mere subterfuges for earning money. In fact, he had cast horoscopes for his own forebears, and compared their lives and character with them. His conclusion that the horoscopes were quite correct shows that Kepler regarded astrology as a valuable method of divination. It is therefore hardly surprising that his own theory of the planetary orbits is somewhat more mystical than Copernicus's idea of a divine wish to express beauty by simplicity.

Kepler was convinced that the creation was based on harmony and symmetry, concepts which appealed to his mathematical mind. It is true that both these concepts have been found useful in modern quantum physics, and that we must not underestimate their significance, but they turned out to be dismal failures in the way that Kepler applied them. He was intrigued by the fact that there are only five regular solids, and he connected it with the fact that there existed only six planets, since he did not know that three further planets still awaited discovery. The perfectly symmetrical solids are the four-sided tetrahedron, the six-sided cube, the eight-sided octahedron and two others with twelve and twenty sides respectively. He drew models of these solids, placing them inside each other in such a way that a sphere touching the corners of one would just touch the planes of the next one. He then found that the ratio of these spheres corresponded to the sizes of the planetary orbits, which convinced him that symmetry must be the basic law which governs the solar system.

This medieval mysticism contrasts sharply with the acute mathematical rationalism in the rest of Kepler's work. He was a mathematical genius who was so profoundly impressed by the geometrical aspect of the Copernican model that he devoted his life to the elucidation of it.

What Kepler needed for his computation of the planetary orbits was the accurate observational data which Tycho had assembled for many years. Tycho's precision of celestial measurements and Kepler's mathematical genius complemented each other perfectly, and the two men fully appreciated each other's worth. When Kepler had been expelled for religious reasons from his position in Graz Tycho welcomed him with open arms at Prague, where he was eventually to become, after Tycho's death, his successor as Imperial Mathematician. Although the two men thought highly of each other, their relationship was not necessarily an easy one. Kepler dearly wished to lay his hands on Tycho's data of the Mars orbit, but the latter was loath to let them go. However, in the end Tycho on his death-bed begged Kepler to complete his work, and two days later the Emperor decreed that all of Tycho's papers should be turned over to Kepler, the new Imperial Mathematician.

Armed with Tycho's data, and his own uncanny mathematical skill and incredible persistence, Kepler now settled down to work out the orbit of Mars. His first result, the discovery of the elliptical orbit, has already been mentioned, and Kepler soon extended his calculation to all the other planets which he also found to move in ellipses, again with the sun in one of the two focal points. Ellipses had of course already been known to the ancient Greeks, and Archimedes showed that, together with the circle, the parabola and the hyperbola, the ellipse arose from the section of a cone. In trying to compute the Mars orbit Kepler had in fact used the equation of the ellipse, and found that it described the behaviour of the planet perfectly. It all fitted in well with Kepler's curious mixture of medieval magic and Greek geometry, which had led him to postulate a solar system based on the five regular Archimedean solids. The ellipse, being so closely related to the circle, confirmed Kepler in the Copernican concept of divine beauty expressed in simplicity. But, of course, he wanted more. He wanted to know not only the geometrical pattern of God's creation, but also its driving force. Here the solution eluded him, for although he soon discovered the key to the mystery, his medieval outlook prevented him from seeing how it had to be turned in the lock.

The discovery that the planets move in elliptical orbits became known as Kepler's first law of planetary motion, and in the years to come he discovered two others. When fitting the ellipse to the Martian orbit, Kepler noticed that the speed of the planet was different in different parts of its path. It was fastest near the sun and slowest at its greatest distance from the sun. Needless to say, the other planets behaved in exactly the

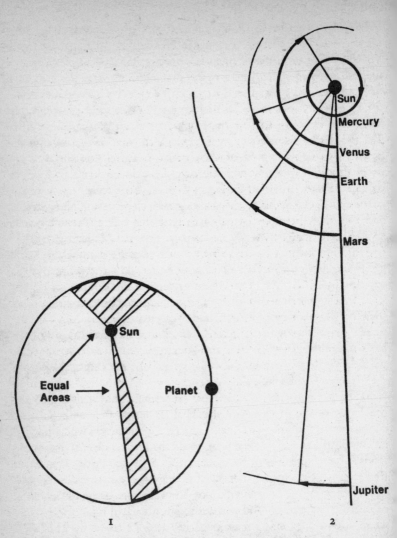

Sun
Mercury
Venus
Earth
Mars
Jupiter

Sun
Equal
Areas
Planet

I   2

Fig. 7. Kepler derived from observation three laws of planetary motion. The first states that the planets move along ellipses with the sun in one focal point (1). According to the second law the distance travelled by the planet is proportional to the area swept by the line, the radius vector, connecting the sun with the planet (the excentricity of the ellipse in our diagram is much exagerated). The third law (2) states that the cube of the time taken for a complete orbit is proportional to the square of the distance between sun and planet. The diagram shows the distances travelled by each planet during a full orbit of Mercury, the planet nearest the sun. The relative distances of the planets shown here are given to scale.

same way. Thanks to Tycho's accurate observational data and to his own meticulous calculations, Kepler was eventually able to formulate a simple law for the variation in planetary speed. He drew the line which connects the sun with the planet, and which is known as the *radius vector*, and plotted the area which this *radius vector* sweeps as the planet moves. It then turned out that the size of this area corresponds exactly to the motion of Mars in its elliptical orbit. In other words, equal areas swept by the *radius vector* correspond to equal times travelled by a planet.

This is Kepler's second law, and he now felt that he was close to the final solution, which he envisaged as a force emanating from the sun and driving the planets along their paths. The further the planet was from the sun, the weaker was this force and the slower was it driven. Kepler's theory had all the makings of a correct solution, except that he did not realize that no driving force is required. His third law relates the speed of the planets with their distance from the sun, and this too appeared to confirm the existence of a driving force originating in the sun and thinning out into space. The law states that the square of the distance is always equal to the cube of the time in which each planet completes a full revolution in its orbit.

The second great step in the development of Western scientific thought had now been taken. The Portuguese had used the new technique of natural philosophy to initiate white domination over the globe. They had scientifically developed the required craft; they had scientifically created the necessary navigational methods; and they had done all this in a remarkably straightforward manner which, at each juncture, was designed to attain the next aim. Their observations and mathematical computations had always been undertaken with direct reference to their practical efforts. Any fundamental speculations in which the members of the Sagres establishment may have indulged were never allowed to distract them from their path along the creation of their sea routes.

The work of Copernicus, Tycho Brahe and Kepler, on the other hand, had not provided them, or the white race in general, with any material advantage. Their observations and computations had solely served as a basis for speculation. Nevertheless, without their advance in fundamental scientific knowledge, the trend set by the Portuguese would have remained sterile. White domination was to go far beyond successful navigation of the oceans. It was to consolidate and immeasurably extend this primary effort. In order to accomplish this, an all-embracing knowledge of the forces of nature had to be established, which ultimately allowed the white man to use these forces for his own ends, whatever these might be.

Such knowledge could only be operated successfully on a firm basis of a workable theory of the creation as a whole. A philosophical system had to be devised to encompass the knowledge gained in a logically consistent world picture. Only the possession of such a picture would make it possible to harness the hidden forces for the service of man. Copernicus, Tycho and Kepler had done more than record and calculate the motion of the planets. They had acted with the clear aim of discovering the fundamental mechanism of the universe, and of the phenomena making up our physical world. In this they had eventually failed, but they provided the necessary basis for a universal theory. Kepler's laws of planetary motion contain all the knowledge required to formulate this theory which the intellectual climate of his age had withheld from him. However, the European world was now changing rapidly, and less than forty years after Kepler's death the solution was to be found by a young man, frustrated through enforced idleness in a small Lincolnshire village.

CHAPTER FOUR

The turning-point

Galileo Galilei was the world's first scientist in the modern sense. He was born at Pisa in 1564, the son of an impoverished Florentine nobleman. His father, an able mathematician whose great love was music, tried everything to dissuade his son from following in his footsteps, and instead sent him in 1581 to the university to study medicine. But this attempt met with failure, for it was in the same year that young Galileo discovered the law of the pendulum by timing the swing of a chandelier during a church service against his pulse beat. It was an ingenious experiment, performed spontaneously and without any training by a lad of seventeen. Investigating nature by experiment, correlating the results mathematically, and then verifying them, again by experiment, was the pattern that Galileo established for scientific investigation.

Unlike Tycho Brahe or Kepler, Galileo stood with both feet firmly in the new world of the Renaissance. This magnificent, if inexplicable, change in the mind of European man had its origin in Italy where, almost a thousand years earlier, classical antiquity had breathed its last. There also it received its name *rinascimento*, meaning the rebirth of that ancient glory. This, however, is something of a misnomer. It was not really the ruins and sculptures of ancient Rome, buried in the Italian soil, that were resuscitated, but something entirely new which grew into the spirit of our modern world, and in which Western science and technology were to play the dominant role.

Its first stirrings manifested themselves in the thirteenth-century paintings of Giotto and his school, which replaced with complex scenes the stylized representation in medieval Christianity of the Madonna and the saints. It is significant that early artists like Paolo Ucello and Brunelleschi introduced a scientific device in order to create a more naturalistic impression. They invented the use of perspective, a mathematical construction which produced sufficient depth on a plane canvas to confer on the viewer a sense of looking into reality. Leonardo was fascinated by the possibilities which perspective offered to the artist, and he and his contemporaries gloried in showing the world as they saw it through their eyes. Emphasis on reality, not only in art but in all other aspects of life, became the keynote of the new age.

The Middle Ages had come to an end. An era which had originally begun in the east with the establishment of Byzantium as the capital of the Christian world, and in the west with Charlemagne's Roman Empire of the German Nation, had run its course. The dream of St Augustine's *Civitas Dei*, a kingdom not of this world, which had captivated the mind of European man for so long, was now being finally rejected. Throughout the many centuries that it lasted, the world of the Middle Ages had seen a number of changes, but none of these had been fundamental, none had radically departed from the central idea that temporal life was nothing but a preparation for everlasting life. Thus it was bound to ignore any incursions which stressed the relevance of realistic thought, and attempts to deviate from the basic importance of the eternal life after death all came to nought. When in the first half of the thirteenth century the Emperor Frederick II held court in Palermo, his entourage comprised many Moors and Jews who had inherited the culture of the Graeco-Roman world. This treasure-house of learning was now wide open to European scholars. However, excommunication of the Emperor by the Pope sufficed to close this gate into what appeared as dangerous knowledge to true Christians, and Frederick's effort to widen the mind of the Middle Ages faded even before his own death.

Historians of science have made much of the recent discovery of thirteenth-century schools of scientific thought, led by Grosseteste and Roger Bacon in Oxford and by Buridan and Oresme in Paris. The fact that knowledge of these schools has only come to light through modern research shows, better than any other argument, that their ideas found no response in the intellectual world of their age, and that whatever new ideas were put forward by them remained sterile. In any case these schools were more concerned with philosophical method than with observation. Their mental exercises were akin to the speculation of scholasticism rather than to the recording of experimental data and their mathematical interpretation, as practised by Galileo and his colleagues.

Two branches of observational learning, however, flourished in the late Middle Ages: astrology and alchemy, both of which had their roots in the preclassical antiquity of the Near East. Like science in later ages, astrology strove for prediction but, unlike science, it was based on an unfounded belief in the magical influence of the stars and planets on the fate of men. Kepler, as we have seen, still believed in this, but it is interesting that he tried to put superstition to an experimental test by casting the horoscopes of his ancestors. Unfortunately, the answers came out in favour of astrology, and we cannot today say how much he was subconsciously influenced by his own inclination. It would be salutary to remember that much the same thing is happening only too often in our own time in the case of medical and psychological statistics.

Alchemy, as the prefix of the word indicates, came to the West from the Arabs, and it was the only part of non-Christian knowledge from the court of Frederick II that took hold in medieval Europe. The reason is not difficult to fathom. The Philosopher's Stone, once discovered, would enable baser stuff to be transformed into gold, and even the most devout princes and clerics could not resist the prospect of this bounty. The practice of alchemy was, of course, dangerously near to witchcraft and other heretical pursuits, and the goldmakers were therefore kept under the close patronage and supervision of their powerful protectors. This also served as an additional precaution against industrial espionage in much the same way that, nowadays, reactor development is kept secure by the Official Secrets Act. The really powerful sponsors of alchemy created veritable research centres in which they assembled the most learned practitioners of the craft. The kings of Bohemia, for instance, kept attached to their castle in Prague a whole street of alchemists which to this day retains the name of *Zlata ulica*, the Golden Lane. It is well protected by a deep ravine at its foot, and this location offers a magnificent view from the back windows of the goldmakers' houses which, for a small fee, can now be admired by tourists. Unlike Prince Henry's research establishment at Sagres, the Golden Lane has survived to this day – most probably because its spirit was so profoundly different and its usefulness so much less than that of the former.

From the Renaissance onward, alchemy was going to change gradually into the exact science of modern chemistry. Its progress on this road is punctuated by a number of landmarks. The first, and probably the most important in the history of white domination, was reached in 1313 when Berthold Schwarz, a German monk in Freiburg, fired the first cannon ball. While his invention of this important weapon is attested by an entry in the records of the city of Ghent of that year, Schwarz cannot be credited with the invention of gunpowder. As we have all learned at school, the Chinese knew how to make gunpowder long before but, being peaceful by nature, used it exclusively for fireworks. In fact, the discovery of fast-burning mixtures seems to be very old and not necessarily confined to peaceful purposes. The most famous of these ancient combustibles was 'Greek fire', a forerunner of modern napalm and evidently used in much the same way. The explosive nature of a mixture of charcoal, saltpetre and sulphur was described before 1250 by Roger Bacon, and it is another proof of the limited nature of the Oxford natural philosophy school that it never occurred to them to use this powder as a propellant charge.

The men of the early Renaissance, on the other hand, were fully aware of the revolutionary nature of the new weapon, and in 1336, only twenty-three years after Schwarz's invention, the republic of Florence ordered a number of metal cannons for the defence of their city. While the invention of firearms certainly was to bring about a profound change in the Western world, this change was not nearly so immediate as is often believed. In particular the notion that it was gunpowder which, by breaching the walls of the feudal castles, changed the Middle Ages into the Renaissance is wildly exaggerated. Long before the cannon balls cracked them open, the baronial strongholds had been reduced to insignificance by bankruptcy. The local squires with their self-supporting villages, and their menfolk whom they led in war, had been the solid foundation on which the Holy Roman Empire was built. However, with the growth of towns, their artisan guilds and their merchants, the knighthood had lost its importance and its modest wealth. Faced with ruin, the noble barons now began to muster their men to ambush the trading caravans until the merchants, too, provided themselves with protection by hiring mercenaries. The counts of Hohenzollern, for instance, took up a strategic position in their castle above the gates of Nuremberg until the burghers were strong enough to persuade them to give up their draughty abode and settle peacefully in their midst. In fact, the knights had become a pain in the neck to both Emperor and Church, and many were sent on crusades to the Holy Land where the Mamelukes made sure that they did not come back. Others, slightly more fortunate, had been commanded to christianize the heathen Slavs in the swamps along the Baltic coast. By the time that cannons became a viable weapon there was little for them to do as regards the feudal nobility.

The development of firearms was a slow process because the supporting technology was difficult, and it took rather more than a century to turn them into a viable project. Turning the pages of Bernal Diaz's *True History of the Conquest of Mexico*, we find frequent references to the simultaneous use of the arquebuse and the crossbow. Thus, at the beginning of the sixteenth century gunpowder had not yet ousted the bow-string. The problems that had to be solved were numerous. First of all, gunpowder tended to de-mix in transport, and it was difficult to ram it into the weapon neither too loosely nor too firmly. This trouble was only overcome through 'corning' the powder by first moistening and drying it, and then by breaking up the 'cake' into grains. The urine of drunkards was much in demand as the wetting agent which produced the strongest explosive. Making a satisfactory barrel was another process that had to be mastered. At first bundles of metal rods had to be welded together, and it was a long time before bronze barrels of sufficient size and strength could be cast and bored.

These details are mentioned to show not only that much new knowledge had to be gained, but also that its application required a new type of man, the technological artisan. Only by building up an experienced and numerous artisan class could progress be made. In fact, from gunsmith to aircraft mechanic, the progress of science and technology had to be based on a well-trained, intelligent army of skilled experts, for these were essential in underpinning the basic ideas and inventions of scientists. In the history of white domination, the development of this class has played a key role which is generally neglected when the advance of scientific thought is considered. Much of this thought could never have arisen without the solid basis of experienced craftsmanship to provide the previous step in the gathering of knowledge. It is significant that many outstanding inventions, from the Renaissance to the Industrial Revolution, were made by largely self-taught artisan technicians.

One of the great achievements of the Renaissance was the opportunity it gave to this type of man, and it may be a sign of the moribund state of Western civilization that the artisan technician, to whom we owe so much, is no longer encouraged. Instead, his initiative is denied scope, and he is placed lower in the social scale than the assiduous, if unimaginative, collector of academic degrees.

Being able to make guns and fill them with powder of a composition suitable as a propellant charge for the cannon ball were only the preliminaries to firing the weapon. Then the real problem arose: to make the missile land at the desired place. This required prediction, and it was here that Galileo introduced modern scientific method into the problem. He showed that the trajectory of a projectile is a parabola, a mathematically well-defined curve which had been known since Greek antiquity. Historians of science have been arguing forever whether Galileo

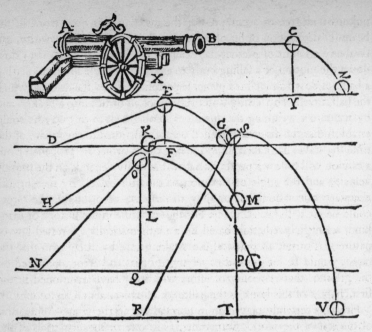

Fig. 8. *Before Galileo approximate solutions, consisting of a combination of straight lines and circular paths, were used to compute the trajectory of a projectile.*

actually dropped pennies from the leaning tower of Pisa, or whether he watched his brother doing it, or whether neither he nor his brother ever did it at all. It does not really matter. Anyone practising rather than studying science will know that it is only too often quite impossible to say, even a short time afterwards, who contributed this or that part to any particular idea. Except for solutions arrived at in strict seclusion, like Newton's law of universal gravitation, or Einstein's theory of special relativity, scientists tend to discuss their ideas with colleagues, and exactly who said what in the discussion often remains a matter of opinion. So be it with Galileo's pennies. People had said before him that things tend to fall faster the longer they fall, and they had attempted to describe the trajectory as a rising straight line which passed through part of the circle into a falling straight line. It was an approximate solution.

What we do know for certain is that it was Galileo who, by an ingenious experiment, established the law of falling bodies with a hitherto unknown degree of accuracy. For this we have his own word in the beautiful description of his observation which, in its concise clarity, can rival any account of present-day science. His brilliant idea was to slow down the motion of a falling body to easily observable speeds by letting a ball run down an inclined plane. He carefully timed the distance which the ball travelled by letting water run out of an orifice into a beaker, and by accurately weighing the quantities so obtained. In this way he could establish that the distance travelled was proportional to the square of the time the travel had taken. It also means that a projectile propelled from a cannon will follow a parabolic path which only depends on the muzzle velocity and the angle of elevation of the gun barrel. By making the necessary calculation, and angling the cannon accordingly, the target could be hit with fair accuracy. For the first time in the history of mankind, scientific prediction based on a mathematically expressed law of nature was turned to practical use. Making sure by calculation that the target would be hit, instead of relying on trial and error, conferred on the gunshot that economy of effort which we have mentioned in the first chapter of this book as the hallmark of experimental philosophy.

Firearms certainly played an important part in the white subjugation of the rest of the world. Sometimes, as in one of the first trials of the machine-gun, a handful of Europeans could completely rout an army of thousands of tribesmen. However, it should be remembered that the chief use of guns and rifles was made by Europeans in wars with each other, often in their efforts to gain spoils from overseas territories or in disputes over control of these distant lands. The other races generally had the use of these superior weapons only when whites put them into their hands to shoot at other whites. On a hill near Canton stands the 'sea-viewing pagoda' which overlooks the mouth of the Pearl River. From here the Chinese could overlook and shoot down at any British gunboats trying to force their way up the river. The rusty cannons still stand there. They bear the mark, 'Friedr. Krupp, Essen'.

Galileo was an experimentalist rather than a theoretician. He investigated with supreme skill and accuracy how an object falls, but remained less curious about why it falls. He explored the action of gravity but not its nature. Using his own results and Kepler's laws of planetary motion, he had before him all that was needed to formulate the law of universal gravitation, if his mind had worked in this way, but it didn't. In fact, his experiments furnished Galileo with the most important concept of mechanics which later was to become the cornerstone of Newton's work. The discovery that bodies of different weight fall with the same

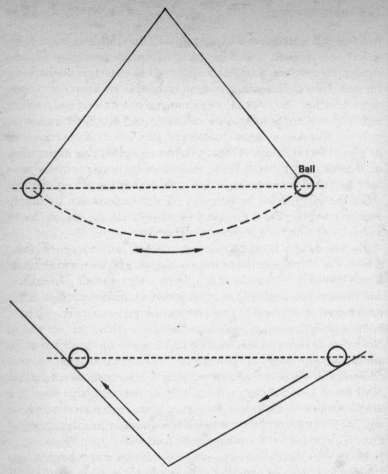

Fig. 9. Galileo discovered that for a swinging pendulum the ball will rise to exactly the same height from which it was released. The same happens when the ball is rolling down an inclined plane and runs up another one, irrespective of the degree of inclination. His conclusion that the 'living force' of a body, as he called it, is always maintained, represents a forerunner of the much wider law of conservation of energy.

speed led Galileo to a clear definition of momentum as mass multiplied with velocity. He, moreover, postulated that this quantity is conserved. A ball that had run down an inclined plane would, owing to this 'living force' which it acquired through its descent, be able to run up another, opposed, slope to exactly the same height from which it had started. When as a young man he had observed the swings of the chandelier, he had seen that a pendulum will rise to almost the same level from which it had been released, and only gradually would the swings become smaller. He concluded that, but for friction, the pendulum might swing for ever. How clear he was about this is stated in his *Two New Sciences* when he writes, 'Any velocity once imparted to a moving body will be rigidly maintained as long as the external causes of retardation are removed.' This does mean, of course, that such a body should continue its path in a straight line. Although he had seen in his own experiments on trajectories that gravity forces the path of the projectile into a parabola, he failed to comprehend that it also causes the planets to circle about the sun. Instead, he shrugged off this inconsistency by simply assuming without reason that, on a very large scale, the motion due to a body's inertia will not be straight but circular.

The reason why neither Kepler, nor Galileo, nor anyone else, conceived of gravity as a universal force is that it is such a very weak force. If two billiard balls, placed a little apart on a very smooth glass surface, were to attract each other like two magnets and run towards each other, universal gravitation would have been recognized in antiquity. We now know that ideally smooth spheres on an ideally smooth surface will in fact run towards each other, but the best surfaces which we can make are still rough enough to prevent any visible attraction due to this minute force. The only reason why gravity dominates all our actions and observations is that we spend our lives close to a very large mass; the earth. Owing to this immense disparity between the earth and ourselves, man has always recognized that he is pulled down by gravity, but never that the earth is pulled up to him by the same force.

Things were made even more difficult by the fact that not everything falls down; smoke, for instance, rises up. Moreover, while a stone will fall down in air as well as in water, wood falls in air but rises in water. This led to the concepts of *gravia* and *levia*, which were evidently relative properties, dependent on the nature of the moving body and the surrounding medium. Accordingly, it was suspected that the acting force was either imparted by the surrounding medium or had its seat in the moving object itself. In fact, the Galilean momentum was for a long time regarded as the 'living force' of the body.

Failing to observe that the earth moves upwards when an object falls down to it had ruled out the notion of mutual attraction from the very beginning. Instead it was assumed that everything had the tendency to move either towards a centre, such as a falling stone, or to move away from the centre, such as smoke. This 'centre' was tacitly assumed to be the centre of the earth, and this idea allowed even for the existence of the Antipodes, which had been proved to exist by the Portuguese voyages of exploration. 'Down' simply meant the direction towards the centre of the globe.

This was all tolerably consistent as long as the earth remained the centre of the universe, but things were very different once Copernicus had moved it away from this exalted position. Before Copernicus people knew why sun, moon, planets and stars did not fall down on earth – they were attached to solid crystal spheres. However, once Copernicus had placed the sun in the centre, it was difficult to understand why the earth, which was clearly not attached to any crystal sphere, did not fall 'down' to the sun.

Historians usually hold that the opponents of the heliocentric system were motivated by some mistaken belief according to which man was placed by God in the middle of the universe. However, when the members of the Holy Office used this argument, they evidently did not realize that they could have employed a much more convincing one. Scientifically it had become impossible to reconcile the Copernican system with the current concept of gravity as the tendency to move towards the 'centre'. One of the two had to be wrong, but very few people seem to have speculated on this unpleasant dilemma. Not for the last time in the history of their subject, scientists pretended not to recognize this discrepancy, and men like Galileo, who was a convinced Copernican, wisely stayed away from formulating theories. He clearly felt that if, at astronomical distances, straight lines became circles, planets and the earth might not have to fall into the common centre.

In our age, when the concept of universal gravitation has become a basic item in everybody's education, it is difficult to comprehend the immense intellectual feat that was involved in its recognition. The falling of an object had to be linked to the motion of far distant planets by a force acting between all masses, a force too weak to be observed in the laboratory. As everybody knows, this momentous step was taken by Newton, and the discovery of action at a distance became one of the cornerstones in the edifice of Western science. Till then, people had regarded gravity merely as the 'tendency' of objects to move down, or possibly up. This was now replaced by a force that worked unseen and without touch over immense distances through the void. It was this action through empty space which, even in Newton's day, many of his colleagues found hard to accept. A few years earlier, the great French philosopher and mathematician, René Descartes, had filled the void with ethereal vortices which moved the planets on circular paths ordained for them by God. Newton himself was aware of the conceptual difficulty posed by the void when trying to explain how light can reach us from the sun, and he postulated light rays as being composed of a shower of tiny particles. This theory was soon discarded in favour of the wave theory of Christian Huygens, a contemporary of Newton's. It was left to Einstein's famous paper of 1905 on the quantum nature of light to revive, in a new form, Newton's corpuscular theory of light.

In addition to fundamental contributions in mechanics and optics, Newton also invented a basically new mathematical method: differential and integral calculus. All these achievements were compressed into a time interval of less than eighteen months, when Newton was twenty-three. The astonishing youthfulness of the discoverer was a fact which has constantly recurred in the history of Western science, and is one of the essential reasons for the West's ability to dominate other civilizations. In science the genius has to be young, and we cannot find a better illustration for this curious requirement than the case of Newton.

Isaac Newton was born at Woolsthorpe near Grantham, Lincolnshire, in 1642. He was a weakly infant with a somewhat disturbed childhood, his father having died a few months before Isaac's birth. His mother married again three years later and left her son in the care of his grandmother. When Newton was fourteen his mother returned to Woolsthorpe after the death of her second husband, the Rev. Barnabas Smith. It appears that his mother's desertion of him at her second marriage profoundly affected the boy, since later at the age of twenty he wrote in his secret confessions: 'Sin No. 13. Threatening my father and mother Smith to burne them and the house over them.' The mother, Hannah Newton, having inherited money from Barnabas Smith, added to the land at Woolsthorpe and wanted Isaac to become a farmer. However, at school the boy had developed a burning interest in mathematics from which he could not be deflected, and in 1661 his maternal uncle, who had been at Trinity College, Cambridge, secured matriculation there for Isaac as a subsizer. This was a position in which the student was paid for serving in college, and three years later Newton became a scholar, taking the degree of Bachelor of Arts in 1665.

Newton was fortunate in having finished his studies when he did, because in the same year the university was closed as it was threatened by the great plague. Newton returned to his mother's house at Woolsthorpe, and so began those remarkable eighteen months of achievement, during which he made essentially all the momentous contributions to science and mathematics with which his name is linked. In later life he wrote of this period: 'All this was in the two years 1665 and 1666 for in those years I was in the prime of my age.'

There are few instances in which we can pinpoint as clearly as this the conditions for the development of scientific genius. A highly gifted young man was sent to a famous university where he received outstanding tuition for four years. His teacher was Isaac Barrow, the Lucasian Professor, who himself was a noted mathematician and who, a few years later, was elected to a fellowship in the newly founded Royal Society. Thus while still a student Newton became fully acquainted with the contemporary state of science and with the salient problems of the day. Then came the enforced break in his studies, and Newton was sent back to Woolsthorpe to be alone, but with his head crammed full of all the relevant facts. His links with the university were temporarily severed, which meant that he was saved from having his mind running into the groove of current scientific speculations. At the most fertile stage of a young man's power of reasoning he was forced to think in isolation, and at the same time he was well fortified by his recently accumulated knowledge. Moreover, there were no distractions, and Newton was free to do what he liked best with the remarkable powers of concentration of which he was capable.

It was in the garden at Woolsthorpe where, one evening, Newton saw the apple fall and wondered why the moon remained up in the sky. That the story is authentic we know from the notes of William Stukeley in 1727, to whom Newton himself told it. In May 1666, after one year at Woolsthorpe, Newton wrote: 'I had entrance into the inverse method of Fluxions and in the same year I began to think of gravity extending to the orb of the Moon.' On his return to Cambridge he pursued his work on optics, and in 1672 submitted it to the Royal Society to which he had been elected a few months earlier. On gravitation, mechanics and calculus, however, he published nothing for many years to come. Nevertheless, he had evidently discussed his ideas on these subjects with Barrow and his Cambridge colleagues since, when in 1669 Barrow vacated the Lucasian chair, Newton was elected as his successor at the age of twenty-seven.

In cramming all the outstanding achievements of his life into an incredibly short time at the very beginning of his career, Newton does not stand alone. We have seen that Copernicus's concept of the heliocentric system came to him when he was a young man, studying at Bologna. Albert Einstein, working on his own in the quiet atmosphere of the Berne patent office, published, before he was twenty-seven, his revolutionary work not only on relativity but also on the quantum theory. Theirs are not isolated cases. In fact, as we have seen, the outstanding advances in science made by men in their young years are the rule rather than the exception. When the great theoretical physicist Lev Landau was shown the work of a man of whom he had never heard, he asked about his age. Told that the author was twenty-eight, Landau said sadly: 'How terrible, so young and already so unknown.'

We have discussed Newton's case in some detail because it provides such a clear example of what goes into the making of a scientific genius. He was favoured not only by having a brilliant intellect, but also by receiving excellent teaching and then, most important, being placed in a position of mental isolation in quiet surroundings. Not every great scientist experienced all these circumstances in his youth, but almost all of them needed conditions which permitted immense concentration in those few precious years when they enjoyed their maximum power to recall accumulated fact. Isolation, often self-imposed, also allowed their imagination to range freely, not yet hedged in by the overpowering force of conventional ideas. Once a scientist has missed this phase in his life he usually stands a poor chance of making a fundamental contribution.

This need for the scientific genius to be young tends to set natural philosophy apart from the moral philosophies. The great civilizations of the East, as well as of the Western world up to the Renaissance, relied for guidance on sages who had acquired wisdom through a long life. Regard for the wisdom of the elders dates from the early age of humanity, when the leader had to pass through successive stages of tribal initiation. Experience rather than the new ideas of the young was taken as the surest guide. This has probably remained true in Western civilization even up to our own age, but there is no getting away from the fact that the white man's way to world domination has relied on the young scientific genius. Neither can we see that this pattern will change as long as science remains the method which dominates our own society. Experience, of course, counts in science, too, and it would be folly not to take note of the subsequent achievements of Newton or Einstein. However, these achievements were basically different from the early bright flame of genius. The scientist in his later years also acquires wisdom, the wisdom of operating the scientific method. This, however, is something that must not be confused with the original divine spark.

Although Newton was a secretive and rather quarrelsome man, he did not spend his life in scientific isolation. At that time there lived, not only in England but also in Germany, France and the Netherlands, many outstanding scientists with whom he could exchange ideas and, if necessary, disagree violently. At the age of sixty-one Newton became President of the Royal Society, a position which he held until his death twenty-four years later. The Society's fellows were an active group of men, some following purely academic pursuits, others interested in practical applications and also men of affairs. They were bound together by their belief that the scientific method was the true path of progress for humanity. Academies similar to the Royal Society were founded in France, Germany, Russia and the Scandinavian countries. The oldest of them all, the Accademia dei Lincei, founded in 1603, had to discontinue its activities in 1667 when its sponsor Leopold de Medici was made cardinal. The new thought of the Renaissance had forsaken its native soil of Italy for the free world of northern Europe. The turning-point had come with the trial of Galileo.

Galileo died, a broken man and virtually a prisoner of the Inquisition, in the same year that Isaac Newton was born. His trial was, more than anything else, the clash of two strong personalities: Galileo, the indomitable scientist who was not free of conceit, and Pope Urban VIII, a forceful and intellectually vain prince of the Church. Galileo's had been a life of triumphs, and he was much aware of his successes. The telescope which he presented to the republic of Venice was not his invention, but he had perfected it far beyond the original instruments. He dramatically demonstrated his instrument to the Doge Leonardo Donati when he showed him, from the San Marco campanile in Venice, the cathedral of Padua, twenty-one miles away. The Venetians, being a seafaring people, were much impressed by the new scientific device, and their Senate accorded Galileo a life pension.

His interest in mechanics led Galileo to the design of various types of machines, one of which – a device for raising water – he also built for the Venetians, and he soon became their adviser at the shipyards and at the naval and military engineering establishment of the Venetian arsenal. He invented the first thermometer, in which he made use of the expansion of air as the working principle, and his studies of the vacuum led his successor Torricelli to the invention of the barometer. His fundamental work on mechanics and his contribution to accurate ballistics have already been mentioned. However, he considered his astronomic discoveries to be his greatest achievements, and it was his pride in them that led to the conflict with the Church.

26, 27 Two men who embody the age of science: *far left*, Galileo Galilei (1564–1642), the first 'modern scientist', died the year that Isaac Newton (*left*) was born.

28 The geometrical device of perspective was developed by Renaissance artists to give depth to their pictures, as here in *The Burning of Savonarola* by an unknown Florentine artist, *c.* 1500.

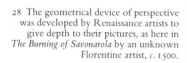

29, 30 Alchemy's claims to be able to transform base metals into gold earned it the respect and patronage of princes. *Left*, an alchemist's laboratory, after a painting by Teniers. *Right*, Zlata Ulica, Prague, the Golden Lane where the King of Bohemia's alchemists lived.

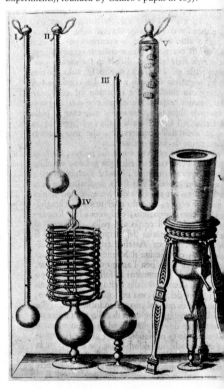

31 Scientific precision is put to practical effect: the setting of the angle of elevation of a cannon illustrated in a sixteenth-century manual on military engineering.

32, 33 *Left*, an astronomical clock in Prague literally brings science to the man in the street. *Below*, a selection of seventeenth-century thermometers and barometers from the Accademia del Cimento (Academy of Experiments), founded by Galileo's pupils in 1657.

34 *Left, Domini Canes* (Watchdogs of the Lord) guard a bridge in Campeche, Mexico. The name was adopted as a sinister pun on the Dominican order administering the Inquisition.

35 *Opposite*, a page of Galileo's notebook showing the position of Jupiter's moons on different dates.

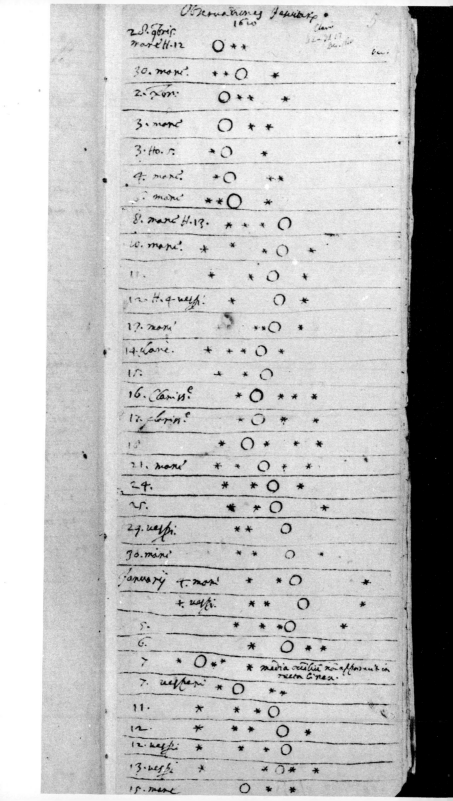

Observationes Jovis
1610

2. 9bris
mane H. 12   O * *

30. mane   * * O   *

2. ♉ri.   O * *   *

3. mane   O * *

3. Ho. 5.   * O   *

4. mane   * O   * *

5. mane   * * O   *

8. mane H. 13.   * * * O

10. mane   *   *   * O   *

11.   *   * O   *

12. H. q. vespi   *   O *

13. mane   * * O   *

14. Cane.   *   * * O *

15.   *   * O

16. Clariss.   * O * *   *

17. clarin.   * O *   *

18.   *   O *   * *

21. mane   *   * O *   *

24.   *   * O *

25.   * *   O   *

29. vespi   * *   O

30. mane   * *   O   *

Januarij 4. mane   *   * O   *

4. vespi   * *   O   *

5.   *   * * O   *

6.   *   O * *

7. * O * *   * media occultii non apparent in
                   recta linea.

7. vespi   * O   * *

11.   *   *   * O

12.   *   * * O *

12. vespi   *   * O

13. vespi   *   * O *   *

15. mane   O * *

36, 37, 38 Accurate and rapid computation is an essential requirement of natural philosophy. *Above*, John Napier (1550–1617), the inventor of logarithms. *Below*, Leibniz's mechanical calculator of 1673. *Right*, Harrison's marine chronometer (1735), which provided the accuracy needed for determination of longitude.

Much has been written about this trial, but one aspect which has been consistently omitted is Galileo's emotional reaction to his discovery. Discovering the satellites of Jupiter, and seeing them circling about the planet, made, as his letter quoted earlier shows, a profound impression on him. And, although we can reason that it is not a strict proof of Copernicus's ideas, Galileo must have felt that he was looking into an entirely new aspect of nature. This aspect was so close to the Copernican system that its impact could not be denied. Only a scientist will be able to comprehend the exhilaration experienced by Galileo in being privileged to be the first to whom this marvel of God's creation was revealed. His adherence to his discovery, even in spite of severe pressure, was not merely pride; it was also the compulsion to insist on the acceptance of a scientific fact on which he felt no doubt.

When describing the life of Copernicus, we saw that the heliocentric system was regarded favourably by the popes of his time, Leo X, Clement VII and Paul III. In fact, the papacy showed no enmity towards the new scientific learning of the Renaissance and, even almost a century later, Paul V showed kindness and consideration to Galileo when he was attacked by representatives of the Church. It was not the hierarchy of the Church that insisted on hounding down Galileo; it was the rank and file. His trial was ordered by the Holy Office, the Inquisition.

Originally a body of the Church charged with suppressing heresies, the Inquisition only became powerful towards the end of the Middle Ages. Just as the barons fought in every way against the changes coming over Europe which were to deprive them of their position, so the monasteries, too, felt these changes as a menace. With many more people learning to read and write, the privileged position of the monks began to wane, and they tried to assert their right to accuse of heresies those who threatened their livelihood. Foremost in this struggle against any innovation was the large and powerful order of the Dominicans who, in the thirteenth century, were given leave by the Pope to organize the Inquisition into a kind of Christian secret police with its own jurisdiction. Accountable to nobody, its proceedings were held in secret and permitted of no appeal. Like all secret police forces, the Inquisition soon became a law to itself and, as often as not, secular as well as ecclesiastical princes began to use this all-powerful institution for their own ends. The Spaniards took the Inquisition with them to the New World and, at Campeche, where the first Christian mass on the American mainland was said, the Dominicans built a little bridge. At each end of the parapet sit fierce-looking dogs, representing a sinister word play on the order's name, *Domini Canes*, the (watch)dogs of the Lord.

With the Reformation came a further threat to the vested interest of the monastic orders, and the violence of the Inquisition increased in severity. There was, however, no special reason why it should have turned against Copernicus. On the contrary, as we have seen, Martin Luther (himself a renegade monk who had married a runaway nun) heaped insult on Copernicus at the same time as the Pope praised the Catholic astronomer canon. It is generally said that in 1600 Giordano Bruno was burnt by the Inquisition because he believed in the Copernican system, but this was declared a heresy only sixteen years later. In fact, Bruno's main heresy was not so much that he was a Copernican but that he had been a Dominican.

In other words professional jealousy rather than religious dogma seems to have been the true cause of the conflict. Galileo's discovery of the Jupiter satellites, mountains on the moon, and spots on the sun, created widespread interest as well as incredulity among his colleagues. Having seen these phenomena with his own eyes, Galileo had little patience with his opponents, whose criticism was based mainly on theoretical argument. He naturally made enemies with his outspoken and occasionally sarcastic replies, and it was only a question of time before one of them would get the idea that Galileo's teaching ran against Holy Writ, an argument that Luther had used against Copernicus a century earlier. Galileo did not ease matters by pointing out that the Bible is not an astronomical textbook, and he was promptly denounced to the Inquisition by a Dominican professor, Father Niccolo Lorini. In the following year, 1616, the Holy Office decreed that it was not the sun but the earth which stood at the centre of the universe, and charged Cardinal Bellarmine to acquaint Galileo with this ruling and to admonish him not to persist in what had now become a heresy.

There is no record of what Bellarmine said to Galileo when he had summoned him to an interview on 25 February, but a few months later Galileo received a paper from the Cardinal saying that the decree of the Holy Office did not constitute an official censure. In the following years Galileo did not bother to hide his Copernican views, and his enemies went on to attack them. While Galileo had powerful enemies, he also had influential friends, and in 1620 one of these, Carlo Maffeo Barberini, a member of one of Florence's most distinguished families, even wrote a poem in honour of Galileo. When, three years later, his friend Barberini became Pope, Galileo felt that the time had come to deal once and for all with the obscurantists who impeded the free discussion of science. In 1624 he set out for Rome to discuss these matters with his now all-powerful friend who had become Pope Urban VIII.

The popes of the Renaissance had taken to the new spirit of the age like ducks to water. Led by the incredibly profligate, corrupt, but also immensely astute Borgia, Pope Alexander VI, they brought to Rome the most renowned artists – Michelangelo, Bramante, Raphael and many others – to work under the patronage of the Vatican. Like secular princes they assembled at their court the protagonists of learning, and showed a benevolent interest in the new natural philosophy. They also unashamedly used the pontificate as a means to raise their families into veritable dynasties. Alexander VI elevated his four children by his beautiful mistress, Vanozza dei Cattani, to high positions in the Church, and he might even have succeeded in making the papacy hereditary but for his son Cesare's violence and lack of political skill. His daughter Lucrezia certainly acted as the Pope's deputy during Alexander's absence from Rome.

Less crude but equally ambitious, Urban VIII had aspirations to found an ecclesiastic Barberini dynasty. A century had gone by since the Borgia rule, and instead of wholesale murder Urban VIII intended to win his battles through literary taste, intellectual ability and connoisseurship of the fine arts. He embellished St Peter's in Rome with the magnificent canopy of the main altar. But the spiral bronze columns were cast from material ripped out of the Pantheon roof, the only metal construction left from antiquity, and the Romans commented on this act of vandalism with the epigram: *quod non fecerunt barbari, fecerunt Barberini.* Bernini carved the marble pedestals of the columns with shields carrying the Barberini crest of the three bees. Out of the scrolls above the shields peers the face of a woman contorted in expressions of lustful rapture, except in the last tableau, which portrays a laughing infant. This man, Galileo felt, would have an understanding of the new spirit of the Renaissance and its science. In the six long audiences Galileo and the Pope conversed on many scientific subjects, and Urban VIII clearly enjoyed debating subtle points of natural philosophy. However, Galileo was not successful in persuading him to reverse the decision of the Holy Office of 1616. This is hardly surprising since the pontiff's main occupation was politics, from which learned discourse was merely a pleasant diversion. He certainly was not going to antagonize the Dominicans for the sake of some academic detail. Instead he suggested to Galileo that there would be no harm in propounding the Copernican doctrine as hypothetical or, as we would say today, as a 'thought experiment'.

Galileo did nothing for two years, and then set to writing his book on the *Two Chief World Systems*, i.e. the Ptolemaic and the Copernican, coming down heavily on the side of the latter. The book was finished in 1630, but it took Galileo two years to get it published. The Thirty Years' War had divided Europe into two irreconcilable religious camps so that, with the change in the intellectual climate, any target was welcome to the monastic hard-liners, particularly if it was a sitting one. Even so, Galileo might have got away but for an unpardonable lack of common sense as well as of taste. His entertainingly written book consists of dialogues involving three persons, Salviati, being clearly Galileo himself, Sagredo, a deceased friend of Galileo's who feeds him the questions, and a defender of the Ptolemaic system, a somewhat naïve intellect. To make things worse this narrow Aristotelian philosopher is called Simplicio, which can be read as 'simpleton', and expresses all the views held by the Pope in his discussion with Galileo. The pontiff might have overlooked Galileo's near approach to heresy, but in his vanity he could not forgive being intellectually ridiculed, and that in public. Incensed, Urban VIII said: 'He did not fear to make fun of me,' and set the hounds of the Lord upon the impudent professor.

It evidently never occurred to Galileo that he was playing, quite literally, with fire, and at first he tried to shrug the whole thing off, saying that he was too old and weak to travel from Florence to Rome in order to appear before the Holy Office. Soon, however, the seriousness of the situation was brought home to him when the Inquisition informed him that he had better set out on the journey forthwith unless he wished to be conveyed to Rome in chains. So he went, still expecting nothing worse than an enforced revision of his book, which he offered readily. Instead, the court of the Inquisition required him to recant humbly in the hall of the Dominican convent of Santa Maria sopra Minerva. As a mark of its clemency, the Holy Office sentenced the kneeling professor to life imprisonment.

The court was on this occasion presided over by the Pope himself. Possibly Urban VIII derived some satisfaction from showing Galileo who was master, but it is more likely that, having let loose the dogs of the Lord, he wanted to make sure they would not tear his erstwhile friend to shreds. Indeed, Galileo spent only two days in the custody of the Inquisition. He was then transferred to the Villa Medici from where, one month later, he was allowed to go to Siena and placed under house arrest with Archbishop Piccolomini, who was one of his former students. After another six months Galileo received permission to spend the rest of his life in confinement at his own villa at Arcetri, where he died nine years later at the age of seventy-eight.

Immediately after his trial, and while still at Siena, Galileo set to work on his most important book, *Two New Sciences*, in which he dealt with the strength of materials and with dynamics. He completed the book in 1636 and two years later it was published – but not in Italy. Instead, it was brought out by the Protestant house of Elzevier at Leyden. Science had turned its back on the Mediterranean world where it had been born, and migrated to the countries of northern Europe where it was free from the reactionary constraint of the Catholic rank and file in the monasteries.

The rise of scientific thought and method to the pre-eminent position they attained in the course of the seventeenth century completely trans-formed the Western world. In less than a hundred years Europe changed its medieval outlook for a fully developed rationalist state of mind which, in its essential concepts, has remained unchanged to our own time. In the year 1600 England was still governed by Queen Elizabeth, who presided over a society which had remained gothic in both architecture and thought. France was torn by the incessant quarrels of the feudal nobility of the Fronde. In Germany Catholics and Lutherans, religious forces which were both medieval in spirit, prepared for the holocaust of the Thirty Years' War. Everywhere the populace remained completely unaware of the new philosophy of science which was shortly to give them mastery of the world and inconceivable riches. The transformation that was to engulf Europe by the year 1700 would have seemed like life on a different planet to which they had been suddenly transported. In England Newton was about to become President of the Royal Society, a well organized company of brilliant scientists who not only probed the secrets of nature systematically and with much success, but who also advised the state on navigation, shipbuilding, agriculture and a host of other questions. In France Louis XIV had created a modern centralized state, established the Académie des Sciences, and assembled at his court not only outstanding poets and writers but also the new natural philosophers who were to make possible a further drastic step towards rationalism a hundred years later. Germany had been fragmented and laid waste by the ravages of a fierce religious war. However, while some remnants of German culture had found refuge in the Low Coun-tries, a new star was rising in the East. The Hohenzollern Elector of Brandenburg had crowned himself as King Frederick I of Prussia, and one of his first acts was to found the Prussian Academy of Sciences at

Berlin. Now only Italy, which had been the cradle of Europe's new philosophy, was left behind. Not for the first time in history had the narrow self-interest of a powerful but stupid group of men ruined the future of their own society.

Since this is not a history of science but of the thought that brought it into being, our account of the scientific development of the Renaissance has had to be sketchy. We have said nothing about the exploration of the human body or the growth of medicine, and many of the advances of the exact sciences, too, have had to be omitted. However, we cannot leave the subject without discussing two steps that were necessary for, as well as symptomatic of, the establishment of natural philosophy, in practice and also in spirit. They are the accurate measurement of time and the growth of mathematics. It is significant that both these steps were taken in the new home of science and technology, northern Europe.

The first instance in which an accurate timing of events was necessary occurred in Galileo's observations of acceleration in free fall. His ingenious device consisted, as we have seen, in slowing down the motion of a falling object by rolling a ball down an inclined plane. This time interval had to be determined rather accurately in order to establish quantitatively the relation between the distance travelled and the time that had elapsed during the travel. For this purpose he used an improved form of clepsydra, an instrument handed down from early antiquity to measure the passage of time by the rate at which water runs out of a vessel through an orifice. By carefully weighing the amount of water collected, Galileo could measure quite accurately the passage of time between two instants in the travel of the rolling ball. However, he would then still have to 'calibrate' the clepsydra against an accepted standard, such as the rotation of the earth as observed from one noon to the next.

In fact our awareness of the passage of time is governed by this periodic change between light and darkness, and the mysterious 'body clock' which each of us carries is ultimately based on this periodicity. Experiments on men and animals kept in perpetual light or darkness show that their body clocks tend to run slow when the check of day and night is absent. In the first experiment of his youth Galileo timed the periodic swing of the chandelier against another periodicity, that of his pulse beat. Nevertheless, he did not use the pendulum as a time measure when investigating the fall of bodies. Clocks embodying the oscillations of a mass had been used in the fourteenth century or earlier, but they all were less accurate than Galileo's clepsydra. Any mechanical clock consists of an oscillator with a constant time of swing, such as a pendulum, a supply of energy to keep the swing going, usually a weight, and a device which counts the number of swings and then displays them on a dial. It was Christian Huygens who, in 1657, attached such an 'escapement' to the pendulum and thereby invented the pendulum clock which has remained essentially unchanged to our day. That he was fully aware of the importance of his invention is attested by the fact that he immediately patented it.

In the Middle Ages there were not many activities which required people to know exactly what time it was. The sun-dial and the few inaccurate clocks were quite sufficient for their everyday needs. All this changed with the rise of the scientific method, which demanded correlation of measurements. These had to be accurate in order to be useful, and the measurement of time was one of them. In this context it is interesting to note the very limited contact between the West and China provided by the Jesuit Fathers at the court of the Manchu emperors in the seventeenth and eighteenth centuries. The emperors did not allow the priests to preach the Christian faith, but permitted and encouraged the importation and making of clocks. It is equally significant that the presence of the Jesuits did not result in the establishment of a clock industry in China, and their efforts were to be entirely directed to the amusement of the court. Chinese society was not embarking on a life governed by natural philosophy, and did not really care to know how late it was.

The need for accurate time-keeping first arose in the era of maritime exploration. It will be recalled that the Portuguese research establishment sent its scientists to Fernando Po in order to observe the height of the sun close to the equator. In fact, the Portuguese sailors soon learned to determine geographical latitude by the height of the sun at noon. To find longitude, however, is a much more difficult task because noon – and that means the local time – varies with longitude; it comes earlier when going east and later when travelling westward. It soon became clear that the ship's captain, when taking the sun's height, should also know by how much time the local noon differed from noon at home. For this he needed an accurate and reliable timepiece. A large cash prize, offered centuries ago by the Bureau des Longitudes in Paris for determining longitude without the use of a clock, has never been claimed.

Galileo was already fully aware of this dilemma, and offered a solution based on his observation of the Jupiter moons. The movement of our own moon in the sky is too slow to serve as a useful clock, but Jupiter has four moons which move not only against the planet but also against each other. In particular, the sudden disappearance of any of these moons when they move into the planet's shadow provides a pretty accurate time check. Galileo suggested that the constellations of these satellites should be calculated in advance and published in the form of tables which could then be used by the navigators. In the end, however, his scheme, which he discussed with the Spanish government, was never applied because it required the use of a powerful telescope and observations with it at sea. Nor would pendulum clocks work well on a rolling ship, but in 1676 Robert Hooke invented an oscillating system, the balance-wheel, in which the restoring force is not gravity, as in a pendulum, but a spring. This led to an accurate pocket watch that can be carried in any position, and the still more accurate marine chronometer. Here again we see the profound change through which society passed in this age. In 1670 a man usually had to guess what time it was, but by 1700 a great many people had only to put their hands into their pockets to know it quite accurately. Regulating the day by looking at a watch brought with it not only a new economy of effort but also constant reliance on measurement, the determination of time.

When correlating observations, time, of course, is one of the most relevant quantities of which we must have a measure, but this in itself is not enough. Galileo found that the distances a falling body travels are not proportional to the times elapsed during this travel, but to the squares of these times. Thus the correlation between the position of the body and the time that it took to get there is a mathematical function, though admittedly a very simple one. In order to write it down we must use an equation: $s = A \times t^2$, where s is the distance travelled in the time t and A is just a number. We have now made use of symbols which had to be created for the purpose and which must be universally accepted as readily understood by anyone reading the equation. This was done at the very end of the sixteenth century by François Vieta, who not only established firmly the use of our signs for addition (+), subtraction (−), multiplication (×) and division (÷), but also determined, by introducing brackets, the sequence in which these operations should be carried out. At about the same time Arabic numerals, which had the advantage of containing the number 0, came into use. The Romans, besides using a difficult system of capital letters, made their calculations very cumbersome by having no 0. The basic mathematical operations had of course been used for a long time, and fairly complicated solutions of, for

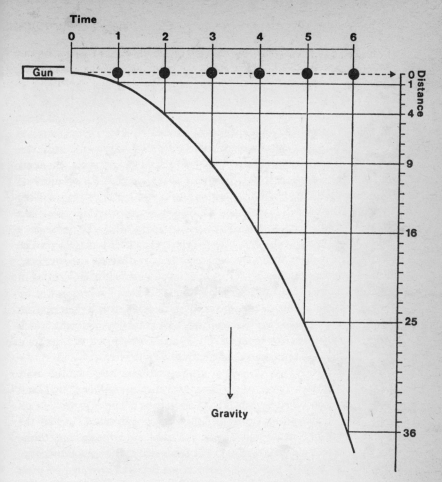

Fig. 10. By careful experiments Galileo showed that the distance through which an object falls is proportional to the square of the time elapsed. A bullet fired horizontally from a gun would cover equal distances in equal times if gravity were not to act on it. However, the force of gravity pulls down the bullet according to the square of the time, and the resulting curve is a parabola.

instance, quadratic equations had been obtained in antiquity. However, awkward and often inconsistent notation saw to it that mathematics remained a pastime of scholars; a learned subject rather than a tool used in practical applications.

However, all this changed with the awakening of the scientific age. Unlike the mathematics of antiquity, which was largely an intellectual exercise, the developments in the Renaissance all tended to be powerful calculating aids. The next step after fixing mathematical notation was the invention of logarithms by John Napier, in 1614. Through this the laborious multiplication and division of large numbers was reduced to the much quicker addition and subtraction of their logarithms. The main application of this elegant method was primarily in computing astronomical observations, but it soon opened new fields of quantitative calculation wherever the time consumed in multiplication or division proved prohibitive. The eagerness with which the new simple calculating method was greeted is shown by its rapid introduction. Calculation by logarithms relies on the use of tables, and by 1624 Henry Briggs, professor of mathematics at Gresham College in London, had calculated such tables to fourteen decimal places. In addition, working together with Napier, he had modified the original scheme into the more convenient common logarithms with the base 10, which are still used unchanged in this form.

The next step was taken in 1637 by the French philosopher René Descartes with his introduction of analytical geometry. Until then the two branches of mathematics, geometry and numerical calculation, had developed largely independently. Descartes introduced the graphic system, which bears his name, of plotting data between rectangular co-ordinates, and this has remained the standard method of displaying observational data to this day. He showed that any algebraic equation correlating two variables can be represented by a curve so that, using as an example our little equation for a falling body, we find that the distance travelled (s) plotted against the time (t) results in a parabola. Needless to say, analytical geometry not only lent itself to the elucidation of planetary orbits, but even more so to ballistics, which had now become an exact science.

Curves in the Cartesian plot represent quantities which change constantly and smoothly, presenting thereby problems with which the old mathematics, which had been dealing with straight lines, could not cope. The first attempt at solving this problem had consisted of dividing up the curve into a great number of straight lines, until finally each of these had shrunk to a point which, however, retained a vestige of the line's inclination. This is the tangent on the curve at this point and, using it as the basis for a mathematical description of the curve itself, Pierre de Fermat developed the mathematical method now known as differential calculus. When a few years later Isaac Newton, in his seclusion at Woolsthorpe, turned his attention to the method of what he called 'fluxions', he based his ideas not only on the work of his teacher

Barrow but also on Fermat's introduction of the tangent as the relevant calculating principle. Determination of the value of the tangent along the curve then leads to a second curve which, when plotted, is the 'derivative' of the first one, yielding information which was not apparent in the original function. Reversing this method of 'differentiation', the area under a curve can be calculated by 'integration'. The principle of calculus leads to a vast and extremely useful field of advanced mathematics which extends the field of classical mathematics, encompassed by the four basic operations of computation.

It will be recalled that Newton had invented differential as well as integral calculus as early as 1666 but, being of a secretive and suspicious character, he published nothing on this work. Meanwhile Leibniz in Germany had developed similar ideas, quite independently, which he published in 1696. In 1673, while in London on a political mission for the Duke of Mainz, Leibniz had been elected to a Fellowship of the Royal Society. Newton suspected, but without justification, that Leibniz had learned about his own unpublished ideas and, being quarrelsome by nature, entered upon a somewhat unedifying controversy as to the priority of the invention. There seems little doubt that, while Newton had developed calculus somewhat earlier, Leibniz, thanks to Newton's secretiveness, had been quite unaware of this work and had invented it independently. The incident provides a pattern that was to occur again and again in the history of science, when important discoveries or inventions were made quite independently and often even in the same month. The reason for this is simple. Science is an organic growth, sustained by a great many people who, of necessity, are thinking on very similar lines. This means that when a discovery is due, it is bound to be made. It does not really matter that a vital clue is sometimes overlooked by one researcher in the field; somebody else will stumble upon it sooner or later, and usually pretty soon.

The importance that the use of numbers suddenly achieved is best shown by a new development: the calculating machine. When in 1673 Leibniz visited London, he showed to Robert Hooke a calculating machine to be exhibited at the Royal Society. It could not only add and subtract but also multiply and divide, and it was the ancestor of all our cash registers and mechanical desk calculators, which only now are being replaced by electronic machines. Already in Leibniz's machine the figures for the operation were set on gear wheels, and by turning a handle the result could be churned out. Leibniz's instrument was the improvement of a mechanical adding device invented thirty years earlier by Pascal. It is interesting that in Leibniz's machine multiplication simply consisted of a great number of rapid additions, a method that forms the basic principle of all modern electronic computers.

It is not an accident, of course, that mathematics developed so very rapidly as new experiments and observations widened the horizon of the Renaissance scientists. At the outset we described the scientific method as the observation of phenomena by the taking of data which then have to be correlated by mathematical operations. It is the unambiguous mathematical equation that constitutes a true law of nature, and it therefore cannot be formulated unless the necessary mathematical techniques have been created first. It is interesting that the type of mathematics produced in the Renaissance was closely related to the practical requirements of the new natural philosophy. Solution of practical problems and ease of calculation were in the forefront of interest. Mathematics had become the most important and the most powerful tool of the new age. It also had become its language.

At the end of the seventeenth century Western man had learned an immense amount about the working of nature, from much of which he had been able to formulate quantitative laws. As yet his newly created philosophy had only helped him marginally in his quest for domination of the rest of the world. Ships had become bigger and better, and they carried cannon, but no advance had been made that could parallel the days of bold ocean exploration and the accompanying development of nautical arts. What now had happened in the West was somewhat similar to the creation of Prince Henry's research establishment at Sagres. But this time the whole of Europe had become a research establishment in which, year by year, new discoveries and inventions were made, potentially capable of an immense concerted effect which could change the face of the world. However, unlike Sagres, there were as yet no clear ideas how and for what purpose the newly developed philosophy of the white race would be used. All progress that was to come was based on the achievements of the seventeenth century. The 'century of genius', as it has often been called, had set the stage, but the action of the drama to be performed on it was as yet unknown. This turned out to be the complete subjugation of the world, and its means was the harnessing of the forces of nature that had just been discovered. Employing them to produce power for man's own use and at his bidding became the ultimate key to world domination. Power production was to the be greatest triumph of the scientific method.

CHAPTER FIVE

Power production, the crucial step

By 1600 probably every man, woman and child in Europe knew that distant lands beyond the seas had been discovered a century ago, and a very large number of people had been personally affected by the opening of overseas trade. Together with this knowledge of strange races, there had arisen an unconscious feeling of superiority over these peoples who had been incapable of withstanding the white onslaught. As yet there probably existed no idea of racial superiority, but rather the conviction that white expansion was a God-ordained process which owed its strength to the enlightenment provided by the Gospels. To their medieval minds it was the mission to save souls which had led the navigators to success, rather than the hidden workings of the Sagres establishment, about which the man in the street knew nothing. Whichever way we look at it, the men of the early Renaissance must have been fully aware of the profound changes that the conquest of the globe had brought, not only to their way of life but, for some, also to their way of thinking. Irrevocably and unmistakably the white race had set itself apart from the rest of mankind, and the special position occupied was, they felt, above that rest.

Unlike the tangible effects of overseas exploration and dominance, the early discoveries in basic science, the advances of natural philosophy, did not touch the population as a whole. To the butcher, the baker and the candlestick-maker, and even to the merchant, it was a matter of indifference whether the earth circled around the sun or vice versa. However, gradually the new skills of the Renaissance began to affect the European standard of life. People in general became richer, and not only because they participated directly or indirectly in the spoils from overseas. Novel crafts and techniques made their appearance and were supported, and perfected, by the new class of scientific artisans who could grind spectacle lenses, make pumps, or work metal. The mineral wealth of the earth under their feet – and not just gold and silver – began to attract people who found mining a profitable occupation. The mines, in turn, required the development of special techniques. One of these was to free the shafts and underground galleries from the water continuously seeping into them. It was here, in fact, that the next great step in the dominant position of Europe was to be initiated. Man and his age-long helper, the horse, began to be faced with tasks that went beyond their power and endurance. Four thousand years earlier, the pyramids of Egypt had been built, using nothing better than the muscle of man. Since then, simple machines, as well as the horse and the bullock, had aided man since antiquity, but the use of wind and water for grinding corn had been his only technological achievement in employing additional power.

Making use of new sources of power demanded not only a willingness to harness the forces of nature but, above all, a knowledge of how to harness them. Power production and manufacturing skills, unlike the discovery of new scientific knowledge, needed more than a few inspired geniuses. Society as a whole had to sustain this next great venture in the progress of European man. To be able to do so, it had to become aware of the problems which until then had only been comprehended by a small group of scientists. But before it could accept the challenge of the industrial age to come, it had to learn what had been achieved by men like Galileo, Newton and Hooke. Their achievements had to diffuse into the minds of the scientific layman so that he could, if he were a banker or an entrepreneur, invest his money in the right way: the way of natural philosophy which guaranteed the maximum economy of effort.

In this process of diffusion of knowledge that became the key feature of the eighteenth century, it would be difficult to overestimate the part played by the learned societies. As we have seen, the first of these sprang up in Italy when, on 17 August 1603, an eighteen-year-old nobleman, Prince Cesi, and four of his friends signed a document founding a society devoted to the study of natural phenomena. Since they were resolved to peer into the secrets of nature with the keen perception of lynxes, they named their association the Accademia dei Lyncei. It seems that Cesi senior, in whose palace the meetings were held, suspected black magic and put a stop to these gatherings. However, the young men persisted in their design. By 1610 the academy was beginning to gain adherents, and on 25 April 1611 it was joined by Galileo as its sixth member. At that time Galileo was already world famous, having published the *Sidereus Nuncius* in the preceding year, and historians have been puzzled that a man who had been awarded a professorship for life by the republic of Venice should have bothered to join this unknown little club. Possibly Galileo sensed that a forum exclusively devoted to the discussion and furtherance of natural science was becoming a necessity in the new age. He may have felt that the faculties of mathematics and philosophy at the universities were too hidebound and theoretical to promote a kind of science dependent both on gathering new knowledge and on turning it to practical application. Certainly the Accademia dei Lyncei opened a new chapter in the history of science, even if it was not going to last. Young Cesi died in 1630, and from then on the Lyncei began to wither, not least as a result of Galileo's trial. The Medici, Galileo's old patrons, still kept an interest in it and tried to revive it in 1657, but when, ten years later, its main sponsor Leopold de Medici was made a cardinal, the academy closed its doors. However, by then the Royal Society and the Académie des Sciences had been founded.

These great national academies, joined later by others in Europe, provided the main impetus leading to Europe's technological advance, though in somewhat different ways. The Royal Society, as we shall presently see, arose from a free association of scientists, or 'virtuosi' as they called themselves, with 'amateurs', who were men interested in natural philosophy but not practising scientists themselves. The French academy, on the other hand, was a government institution, created by Louis XIV at the suggestion of Colbert who, in 1666, invited France's outstanding scientists of the day to meet regularly for the purpose of discussing science and its practical uses, in so far as they were deemed important to the state. For instance, the new Académie provided a detailed demographic survey of France, applying scientific methods such as mathematical surveying and statistics for the first time to economic and political problems. When at about the same time Charles II suggested a similar undertaking to the Royal Society, the scheme came to nothing for lack of funds since the Society received no government grant, and Charles was in chronic financial difficulties. The other national academies all followed the French example of state institutions, granting their members life pensions, whereas the Royal Society from its very beginning charged a fee from its members, a system retained to this day.

On 3 May 1621 the House of Lords had sentenced the Lord Chancellor of England to imprisonment in the Tower and a fine of £40,000 for taking bribes, after the accused had freely admitted his guilt. He was the renowned Francis Bacon, a confidant of the King. James I soon remitted the fine and limited Bacon's stay in the Tower to four days.

However, Bacon obeyed the injunction not to engage again in affairs of state, and for the remaining five years of his life devoted himself entirely to questions of philosophy. He succumbed, in fact, to one of his own experiments when he wanted to see whether putrefaction is arrested by freezing. Embedding a chicken in snow, he caught a cold from which he died, but not before he had recorded that the experiment had been a full success. Bacon's philosophy aimed at the proper investigation of natural phenomena, and at the discovery of connexions between them. In his great work, *Novum Organum*, he visualized an academy, the House of Salomon, in which scientists carried out their experiments and made observations on plants and animals. These 'Fellows' were to be supported by 'Merchants of Light', gathering information from distant lands and seas. England by then had become the foremost seafaring nation in the world, and Bacon's ideas reflect the wish to complement exploration with the kind of research and education demanded by it.

It was in this spirit that a number of young virtuosi used to meet once a week in taverns or coffee-houses in London to discuss questions of natural philosophy or hear reports on strange animals and plants brought from overseas. They included John Wilkins, later Bishop of Chester, the Hon. Robert Boyle, an eighteen-year-old nobleman, and John Wallis who, thirty years later, wrote that subjects barred from discussion at these meetings were 'Divinity, State-Affairs and News (other than what concerned our business of Philosophy)'. On the other hand, they were interested in a multitude of matters such as 'The circulation of the Blood, the Copernican Hypothesis, the improvement of Telescopes, and Grinding of Glasses for that purpose' as well as 'the weight of Air, the Possibility or Impossibility of Vacuities and Nature's abhorrence thereof'. One of their number, Dr Goddard, employed at his house an 'operator' skilled in lens-grinding, and often these virtuosi arranged for experiments to be demonstrated before them. Boyle called their meetings 'the invisible College'.

As a result of the political troubles due to the establishment of Cromwell's Commonwealth, many of these men moved to Oxford where the meetings were continued in Dr Wilkins' lodgings at Wadham College, of which he had become Warden. Boyle set up a laboratory in High Street, where he employed as assistant a hunchbacked young man by the name of Robert Hooke, and it was during these years that Hooke invented the balance-wheel which led to his development of the pocket watch. The meetings were held on Thursdays, and every member had to contribute one shilling for each meeting to pay for the cost of experi-

39, 40 *Left*, Robert Boyle (1627–1691), a member of the so-called 'invisible College', the precursor of the Royal Society. *Below*, the frontispiece, designed by John Evelyn, of Thomas Sprat's *History of the Royal Society* (1667), showing the bust of its founder, Charles II, flanked by its first president, Lord Brouncker (left), and Francis Bacon.

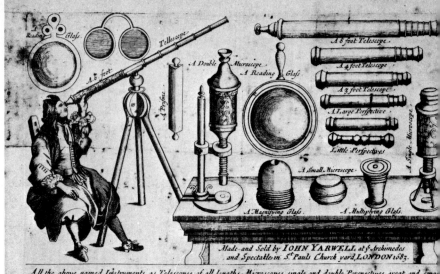

Made and Sold by IOHN YARWELL, at y Archimedes
and Spectacles in St Pauls Church yard LONDON 1683.

All the above named Instruments as Telescopes of all lengths, Microscopes single and double, Perspectives great and small,
Reding Glasses of all Sizes, Magnifying Glasses, Multiplying Glasses, Triangular Prisms, Speaking Trumpetts, Spectacles fitted
to all ages, And all other sorts of Glasses, both Concave and Convex.

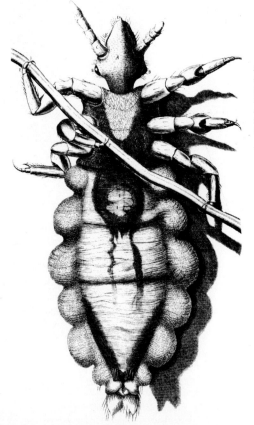

41, 42 Scientific equipment in the seventeenth
century revealed new worlds of the vast and the
minute. *Left*, the drawing of a louse from the
Micrographia of Robert Hooke (1635–1703).
Above, the new profession of scientific
instrument manufacture: John Yarwell's
trade card of 1683.

43 Atmospheric pressure on a vacuum. The burgomaster of Magdeburg, Otto von Guericke (1642–1686), arranged a spectacular demonstration when two teams of eight horses were unable to pull apart a pair of hemispheres from which the air had been exhausted.

44, 45, 46 *Left*, Gottfried Leibniz
(1646–1716), shown holding a paper
crediting him with the invention of
calculus (disputed by Newton).
Below (right), James Watt (1736–1819)
the foremost pioneer of power
production, and (*left*) Benjamin
Thompson, Count von Rumford
(1753–1814), who showed that heat
was not of a material nature.

ments. Among them was a young commoner of the College, Christopher Wren. These Thursday meetings were continued when, after the Restoration, the group returned to Gresham College in London. One enthusiastic amateur, John Evelyn, a friend of the King, suggested to Charles II that he should extend his patronage to the group. This was the beginning of the Royal Society of London to which, on 15 July 1662, Charles granted a charter and the Great Seal, though the first page of the Journal Book bears the date 5 December 1660. John Evelyn designed the frontispiece for Sprat's *History of the Royal Society*, published in 1667. It shows the bust of Charles II, flanked by the first president, Lord Brouncker and Francis Bacon, and demonstrates that the Fellows regarded the Society as inspired by Bacon's House of Salomon. When in 1663 Charles presented the Society with a mace, he defined its purpose as 'the improving of Natural Knowledge by experiments'. This spirit of investigation, unhampered by established authority, is also reflected in the choice of the Society's motto, taken from Horace's *Epistles*, of *Nullius in verba*, which can be extremely freely translated as 'nothing taken for granted'.

In spite of the constant money troubles which beset the first decades of the young Society, it overcame all difficulties and began to flourish. Not all these difficulties were financial ones; attack and ridicule started immediately upon its foundation. In fact, Thomas Sprat's *History* of 1667 was not only an account of the Society's foundation, but was mainly written in defence of its aims and in refutation of its detractors. Foremost among these was a Dr Henry Stubbs, one of the most famous Latinists of his time. Besides calling the Fellows 'very great impostors or men of little reading', he followed in his self-righteous venom the age-old claim to be the guardian of 'the interest of the monarchy and religion in this land, the welfare of the Church or State, the happiness of this generation and of posterity'. In fact, the pattern he set for dire warnings of impending doom arising from science has remained essentially unchanged down to our days. It is interesting that Stubbs was set on his course of diatribes by a Dr Hamey, a member of the Royal College of Physicians who was afraid that the researchers of the Royal Society might invade the province of his own College. While Sprat and some of the Fellows were clearly upset by these attacks on the Society, John Evelyn felt that there was no point in taking note of this 'snarling adversary', and advised his colleagues to 'let the moon dogs bark'.

Rather more damaging than Stubbs and his tirades were the satirists. Even Charles II had good-naturedly railed the Fellows, as Pepys who was president of the Society reported, 'for spending time only in weighing of ayre'. In fact they soon learned that they had to protect themselves against practical jokers who might send fakes or ridiculous objects to be included in the Society's collections. The Society's secretary, Henry Oldenburg, ruled in 1668 that gifts from outsiders could not be accepted, unless first shown to the president, 'for fear of lodging unknownly ballads and buffooneries in these scoffing times'.

In 1673 Thomas Shadwell's play *The Virtuoso* was first performed on the London Stage, where it immediately became a great success. Its main character is Sir Nicholas Gimcrack, a man completely immersed in the new philosophy, very much to the annoyance of his wife who deplores the £2,000 he has spent on microscopes in order to study the eels in vinegar and the mites in cheese. The play was clearly a satire on the Royal Society, as was Samuel Butler's poem 'Elephant in the Moon'. Butler also wrote 'On the Royal Society':

> These were their learned speculations
> And all their constant occupations:
> To measure wind and weigh the air
> And turn a circle to a square.

Even worse was to come with Jonathan Swift's publication, in 1726, of *Gulliver's Travels*. In his scathing condemnation of contemporary life and institutions, he reserved a special corner for science and the Royal Society in the *Voyage to Laputa* with his invention of the 'Academy of Lagado'. There scientific projects are undertaken by 'projectors', as for instance the extraction from cucumbers of sunbeams, to be bottled and later released whenever required. Another project, and one reputed to be already accomplished, was clearly a skit on Leibniz's mechanical calculator. It was a 'word making machine', a square box with a great number of elements and many handles to be turned manually so that, by using it, 'the most ignorant person, at a reasonable charge, and with a little bodily labour may write books in philosophy, poetry, politics, law, mathematics and theology without the least assistance from genius or study'. Gulliver personally had a taste of the new experimental philosophy when a suit of clothes was made for him by this method. Instead of using the tailor's tape, his height was measured by means of a quadrant, and the outline of his body ascertained by compasses. Notes were assiduously taken, but when the suit came it 'was very ill made and out of shape by happening to mistake a figure in the calculations'. Altogether, Swift's projectors busied themselves with the development of new tools and methods in building, manufacture and agriculture; 'but', he says with regret, 'none of the projects are yet brought to perfection and in the meantime the whole country lies in miserable waste, the houses in ruins and the people without food and clothes'.

Nothing can illustrate more convincingly the sudden impact of science on society than these attacks and satires. The fact that less than fifteen years after the founding of the Royal Society, theatre audiences laughed night after night at the eccentricities and harebrained antics of Sir Nicholas Gimcrack, leaves no doubt that experimental philosophy and its practitioners had become objects of popular interest. In order to become amusing, there had to be a public awareness of science, encompassing wide circles of contemporary society. Ridiculing scientific methods required general knowledge of their existence. Unlike the scholars of the previous century, whose names were known only to a few colleagues, the Fellows of the early Royal Society were public figures. To some extent this was a result of the mixture of virtuosi and amateurs, i.e. professional scientists and men of affairs, but it is significant that their meeting ground was science and not affairs. In other words, these amateurs felt that experiments and collections of rarities were an essential part of the intellectual life of their time. A new world was opening up before their eyes. It was a world of inquiry, and at the same time they sensed the coming mastery over the forces of nature that experimental philosophy was going to give them.

The Royal Society's collection of rare creatures, plants, rocks and other curiosities, too, soon elicited public interest. Sir Hans Sloane, who followed Newton as president, augmented them from private funds and they grew to such extent that they filled a large house in Bloomsbury. They had to be taken over by the government and were opened to the public in 1754, forming the beginning of the British Museum, of which to this day the president of the Society remains a trustee. The Royal Society was also instrumental in establishing and fitting out the Royal Observatory in Greenwich which Charles II had founded after Flamsteed had drawn his attention to the inadequacy of the existing star catalogue. Charles realized immediately the importance of reliable astronomical data for overseas navigation, and ordered £500 towards the building of the observatory. As was to be expected, the money did not go far, and the Fellows of the Society furnished it with their own private instruments.

However, from its very beginning as 'the invisible College', the main occupation of the Royal Society had been with the conduct and demonstration of experiments. Wilkins showed that a man sitting on a pig's bladder could be lifted bodily by merely inflating the bladder with human breath, thus drawing attention to the use of air as a working agent. Christopher Wren, before being absorbed by his career as an architect, was much interested in the transfusion of blood and conducted numerous experiments which ultimately led to the technique of intravenous injection and the clinical provision of blood to a patient. For all these experiments competent and inventive 'operators', as they were called, were required, and the virtuosi in many cases had skilled men of this kind working in their pay and often in their houses. The most famous of these was Robert Boyle's assistant, Hooke, who not only became one of the most illustrious Fellows of the Royal Society and eventually its secretary, but who had also already played an important role in the days before its foundation.

The immense variety of subjects to which Hooke turned his attention is truly bewildering, and they covered the practical as well as the theoretical aspects of science. His invention of the balance-wheel has already been mentioned. It was supplemented by the development of the anchor escapement that was incorporated in the pocket watch, and on the way he discovered the basic law of elasticity which bears his name. His perfection of the microscope and researches in its use led to the publication of his *Micrographia*, while his work on the iridescent colours of thin films convinced him that light was a wave motion, contrary to Newton's ideas of its particle nature. He showed that the force of gravity could be measured with a pendulum, and thus discovered universal gravitation later than, but independently of, Newton. Equally important is Hooke's suggestion that heat might be a state of motion, and thermal expansion a general property of all substances. He also invented a form of aneroid barometer, and used its readings for weather forecasts.

Hooke has often been accused of leaving too many of his divers researches unfinished. Since he became Gresham professor of geometry, Cutlerian lecturer of the Royal Society and, after the Great Fire, surveyor for the rebuilding of London, he had some excuse for leaving things unfinished. Whether he really did so we do not know since, for fear of losing pecuniary advantage, he kept much of his work secret. However, his most time-consuming occupation was the provision of experiments for the Royal Society, whose curator he had become in 1662. Shortly afterwards he was given free lodging at Gresham College, which he let later to the Royal Society for £10 per annum. Hooke was as secretive as Newton, and more irascible. In fact, Newton delayed the publication of his *Optics* until after Hooke's death 'to avoid being engaged in disputes about these matters'.

While the Royal Society possesses excellent portraits of all its famous Fellows, none of Robert Hooke exists. According to Richard Waller, who knew him in his later years, Hooke was 'as to his person but despicable, being very crooked', and that 'he was always very pale and lean, and laterly nothing but Skin and Bone, with meagre Aspect. . . . He wore his own hair of a dark Brown colour, very long and hanging neglected over his Face uncut and lank.' In spite of his prodigious scientific work we knew practically nothing about the personal life of this remarkable man until fairly recently, when Hooke's own diary, covering the years 1672 to 1680, came to light. It is entirely composed of short sentences in telegram style, but gives a wealth of information about his activities and meetings with his colleagues, mentioning more than 150 London coffee-houses and taverns where they foregathered. Moreover, it reveals that Hooke was a tortured hypochondriac who took a multitude of remedies, and carefully recorded their effects (such as headaches, vomiting and sweating) and that he was equally meticulous in listing his reactions following intercourse with the housekeeper. But apart from presents of cloth to her, Hooke appears to have been very miserly, and this impression is reinforced by his complaints of irregular payment by the Royal Society. On the other hand, he occasionally mentioned his intention of making a will in its favour so that the Society could be housed in splendour, an idea that was not taken too seriously by his contemporaries, in view of Hooke's impoverished appearance. Nevertheless, after he had died intestate a chest was found that had been locked up for at least thirty years, containing many thousand pounds in gold and silver. The death in 1687 of his niece Grace, who had kept house for him and had been his only close companion, made him more lonely and eccentric than ever until his death in 1703 at the age of sixty-seven. D'Alembert wrote to Fontaine: 'Hooke est mort – c'était un homme de génie, et un mauvais homme, la Société y gagne plus que la géometrie n'y perd.'

In his notes Hooke records that 'in 1658 or 9, I contriv'd and perfected the Air pump for Mr. Boyle', and it was in this work that the foundations of power production were laid. The story may or may not be true that James Watt, a century later, was led to the idea of a steam engine when as a boy he watched the lid of a kettle being lifted by steam. But it has no significance for the history of power production, particularly since the early steam engines were not driven by steam but by the pressure of the atmosphere. The real story starts with the activities of the invisible college when they discoursed, as John Wallis noted, on 'the Possibility or Impossibility of Vacuities and Nature's abhorrence thereof'.

Late in life Galileo began to be much interested in exactly this question without, however, getting the final answer to it. When he blamed the Duke of Tuscany's pump-maker of poor workmanship, the man replied that, as was well known, no pump, however excellent, could draw up water for more than twenty-seven feet, a statement with which Galileo eventually had to agree. But his explanation for this phenomenon was the wrong one. He believed that, as a very long rope would eventually break under its own weight, so the column of water in a vertical tube must rupture under its own strain. Nevertheless, the vacuum played some part in the process, since Galileo believed that the strength of materials was due to some internal vacuum caused when one tries to pull the substance apart.

The thesis that a vacuum cannot exist in nature had originated with the Greeks and was maintained throughout the Middle Ages. It clearly required a major intellectual step to assume that the space between the planets was empty, and that an atmosphere of air enveloped the earth in much the same way that water covers the depths of the oceans. It seems that this step was taken some time at the middle of the seventeenth century, and Galileo himself may have been convinced of it at the time of his death. Torricelli, who had been close to Galileo during the last months of the latter's life, certainly performed the crucial experiment in the following year. He replaced the Duke of Tuscany's pipe by a glass tube, and the water in it by mercury. When the tube, whose upper end had been sealed, was lifted from a trough filled with mercury, it was found that the mercury could not rise above about 30 inches. The space above the mercury was empty and became known as a Torricellian vacuum. In fact, as Torricelli pointed out, his trough simply acted as a pair of scales: on one side rested the weight of the atmosphere, and this was balanced on the other by the weight of mercury 30 inches high. The apparatus has since become known as a 'barometer'.

This brilliant demonstration that atmospheric pressure is the weight of the air above us was further confirmed by an ingenious experiment carried out at the suggestion of Blaise Pascal. A barometer was carried up to the top of the Puy de Dôme, 4,800 feet above sea level, and taken down again on the same day. At the top the barometer showed a much lower reading than at the foot of the mountain, proving that the weight

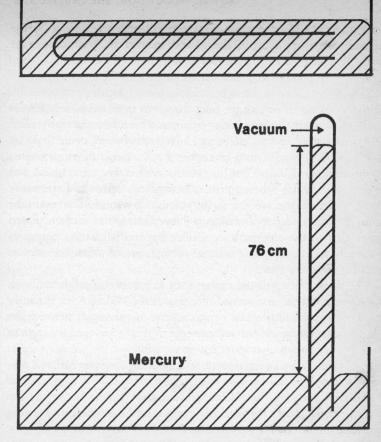

Fig. 11. Torricelli, a pupil of Galileo's, raised a glass tube, sealed at one end, out of a trough filled with mercury. He observed that the mercury in the tube rose only to a height of 76 cm., while the space above it remained empty. He had created a vacuum, and, incidentally, invented the barometer. The arrangement represents a balance on which the weight of the atmosphere is equal to the weight of the mercury column.

of the column of air was less at a higher altitude. The existence of the earth's atmosphere had thus been established beyond doubt only five years after Torricelli had postulated it. Experimental philosophy was beginning to get results quickly.

Meanwhile, and independently, another attempt was being made to disprove nature's abhorrence of a vacuum. Otto von Guericke, the burgomaster of Magdeburg, was spending a fortune of £40,000 on the construction of air pumps and experiments with them. The most famous one was made with two strong-walled hollow metal hemispheres whose rims had been ground so flat that they made an airtight fit. He then pumped the air out of them and demonstrated to a large audience the pressure of the atmosphere, pressing the hemispheres together in a most spectacular manner. Twelve horses tethered to each hemisphere were not strong enough to pull them apart. In another experiment Guericke used a cylinder with a close-fitting piston, and showed that very great force was required to pull out the piston since it was pushed back into the cylinder by the pressure of the atmosphere. Unlike the experiments of Torricelli and Pascal, Guericke's demonstration drew public attention to the immense force provided by the weight of the atmosphere, and it was bound to raise the question whether it might be possible to harness this pressure. The weight of air now became a matter of serious interest, opening up speculation of turning it to use, and King Charles's quip about the Royal Society 'spending time only in weighing the ayre' no longer referred to an idle and ridiculous pursuit. Charles could hardly have known that thirty years later the British government would grant a patent for a steam engine utilizing the weight of the air for pumping water out of mines.

The Hon. Robert Boyle, fourteenth child of the great Earl of Cork, travelled to Florence at the age of fifteen to study the works of the 'great star-gazer' Galileo. Galileo himself was still alive, though there is no record of young Boyle visiting him. But he may then have met Torricelli, who later came to London. After his return to England Boyle carried out his famous experiments on the 'spring of the air', which established the law of the elastic properties of gases that bears his name. The practical work was largely done by his assistant Hooke, whom Boyle did not treat as a mere 'operator' but as a close friend till his own death in 1691. No two men could have been more different in temperament and outlook, but the burning interest in their scientific work resulted in a most fruitful collaboration. Both of them were concerned with the harnessing of atmospheric pressure for power production, and Hooke, at least, lived to see its practical realization.

Whereas the Portuguese opening of the sea route to India had been a carefully planned undertaking with a clear aim in mind, the next great step in world domination, power production, had a fitful start. Spices from overseas had become essential for preserving Europe's meat over the winters, but power other than that provided by men and their beasts, or by wind and water, had not yet become a burning necessity. The discovery of new energy sources had brought into the realm of possibility new means of providing power, but there was as yet no strong incentive for their development. They came into being as an exercise in the use of natural philosophy rather than as an economic proposition and, as we will see, their purpose was not immediately recognized. In fact, for a time steam engines were used to pump up water for the paddle-wheels of textile mills, instead of driving the mills directly.

Nevertheless, the experimental itch of natural philosophy could not leave power production alone, whether it was useful or not. Making use of gunpowder to drive a machine instead of merely firing a cannon was an obvious choice and Christian Huygens, the great Dutch scientist, who was then at the French Académie des Sciences, had a go at it. He handed the job to a young medical doctor, Denis Papin, who in 1671 was appointed as assistant at the Académie but who failed dismally in his attempt to create a vacuum by firing off gunpowder. Its force was too large and too quickly released to permit the construction of vessels that would contain it, very much like the difficulties experienced in our day in harnessing the fusion reaction of the hydrogen bomb. All hopes of turning explosions into power-producing machines were given up, and the world had to wait another two centuries for the internal combustion engine.

Papin, who was a Huguenot, left the Académie in 1675 for London where, not unnaturally, he turned to Robert Boyle and the Royal Society. It will be recalled that, in addition to his (and Hooke's) pre-occupation with air pumps and the vacuum, Boyle had made important studies on the elastic properties of gases, and it was evidently these which set Papin on his work of boiling water in a completely closed vessel. He discovered that both the pressure of the steam and the temperature of the water rose, and the apparatus became known as 'Papin's pot'. It is still used in its original form for class-room demonstrations. Papin also found that cooking food in his pot at an elevated temperature softened even bone and gristle. He had invented the pressure cooker which, at Hooke's invitation, he demonstrated before the Royal Society under the name of 'bone digester'. John Evelyn, who partook of 'this philosophical supper', comments in his diary not only on the excellent taste, the fact that they ate 'pike and other fishbones, and all without impediment', but also on the great saving of fuel in its preparation. Three years later, in 1684, Papin was made temporary curator of the Royal Society, but in 1687 he left London to accept professorships first in Marburg and then in Cassel. Papin's next invention was published in 1690, but it is clear from a communication to the Royal Society in 1687 that he owed its inception to the collaboration with Boyle. He had invented a simple way of creating a vacuum and of making the atmospheric pressure drive an engine.

Papin realized this achievement by combining his own experiments on steam with Otto von Guericke's arrangement of a cylinder with a tightly fitted piston. However, instead of evacuating the cylinder with an air pump, he filled the space under the piston with water and then heated the cylinder in a fire. The water evaporated into steam which drove the piston out as far as a stop fitted to the cylinder. When now the cylinder was cooled, the steam in it condensed again to water and the atmospheric pressure pushed the piston back with its full force, thereby providing the working stroke of the engine. The steam engine had been invented, only it was not yet called a steam engine but a fire engine.

In Papin's engine the steam had only served to create the vacuum, while the work was done by the atmosphere. The machine itself had grown step by step out of the experiments and theories of natural philosophers, and it is not surprising that it was immediately given its correct scientific name which, in all its various forms, it has retained to this day. It was fully realized that the work which it could furnish was provided by the heat supplied to the cylinder and, since at that time the word 'fire' was used to describe heat, the original description, turned into modern parlance as heat engine, is the correct one.

The tangled history of the steam engine itself has been written so frequently and competently that we shall not follow it in any detail, but a few less well-known aspects deserve a mention. How clearly Papin foresaw the prospects of his invention is shown by his memoranda to the Royal Society. After first having communicated, in 1687, the idea of a heat engine to raise water from the mines, in 1708 he suggested to the Fellows the construction of such an engine for a number of practical applications, which included a boat driven by paddle-wheels. The bland statement generally made by historians of science that the Royal Society turned down this proposal owing to lack of interest and funds can bear with amplification. The proposal was, in fact, discussed at length and the president, Newton, wrote to Leibniz, who was a Fellow resident in Germany, for advice. Leibniz then replied by comparing Papin's engine with the one built by Savery and demonstrated before the Royal Society in 1699. He concluded that Papin's engine appeared to him worthy of consideration, and that he would be prepared to have one built – if the Royal Society were to pay for the construction and for his own work. The matter was again debated under Newton, who was favourably inclined towards Papin's engine but said: 'But the force and uses of the engine must be learned gradually by trying the simplest and cheapest experiments first, and reasoning from those experiments.'

Newton, of course, was right. At the time of Papin's proposal, Savery's engine, called 'the Miner's Friend', had been demonstrated to work, and Newcomen was constructing another engine for pumping water out of mines which came into practical operation in 1712. In other words, inventors who were going to promote heat engines had entered the field with the idea of paying for the development out of their commercial proceeds. The Royal Society had provided the forum where the basic ideas of power production had been discussed and brought to a stage at which promoters could take up the practical development – as indeed they did. It might have been to the financial advantage of the Society to carry out this commercial promotion itself, but it can hardly be held that inactivity in this matter amounted to the neglect of scientific progress. The promoters were already on the spot and, as it turned out, the real economic need for power production was not to come for another century.

Both Savery's and Newcomen's engines employed the principle of creating a vacuum by steam which Papin had already published in 1690. Savery had used a tandem method of heating and cooling cylinders, and Newcomen accelerated the condensation of steam by spraying cold water into the cylinder. A most important improvement was made in 1763 by James Watt who, instead of condensing the steam inside the cylinder, let it out into a separate condenser. This increased the efficiency enormously, since the cylinder was kept hot all the time and far less fuel was needed for the engine. This solution had in fact already been proposed by Papin, whose grasp of the physical principle of the heat engine was much superior to that of Savery or Newcomen. Watt's second great invention came a few years later. Instead of relying on the atmosphere to push down the piston, he used steam pressure not only underneath the piston but also above it. In this double-acting device steam was now the sole working agent, and it thus became the first true 'steam engine'.

Nothing much more need be said about steam engine development, which in due course moved on to high pressure engines and steam turbines. The particular advantages offered by these could only be understood after the physical theory of heat as a form of energy had been

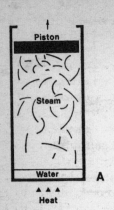

A

Heat removed

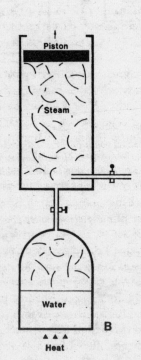
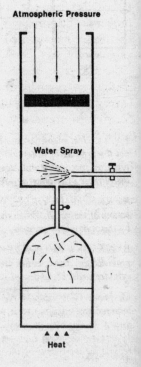

B

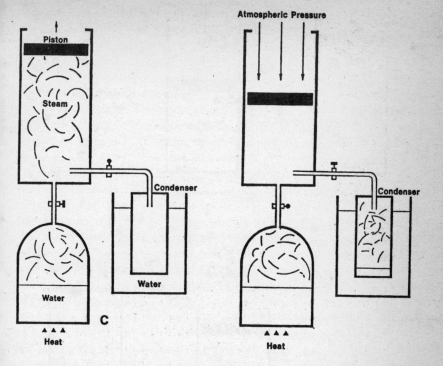

Piston

Steam

Condenser

Water

Water

C

Heat

Atmospheric Pressure

Condenser

Water

Heat

Fig. 12. Heat engines are our means of power production. In the early heat engines it was not the pressure of steam which provided the work but the pressure of the earth's atmosphere. A space filled with steam which could then be condensed into water merely served the purpose of creating a vacuum against which the atmospheric pressure could act.

A. Papin filled a cylinder, fitted with a piston, with steam by boiling water in the bottom of the vessel. When the cylinder was allowed to cool, the piston was forced down by the atmospheric pressure.

B. Newcomen improved Papin's design by separating the cylinder from a boiler which provided the steam. When the steam supply was cut off by a tap, the steam inside the cylinder could be condensed rapidly by a spray of cold water.

C. James Watt adopted Newcomen's principle of separate boiler and cylinder, but improved the efficiency greatly by allowing the spent steam to pass into a separate condenser. In this way no energy was lost by cooling the cylinder. Only at the next step, Watt's double acting engine with steam on both sides of the piston, did steam pressure replace the work done by the atmosphere.

worked out scientifically. Watt's own contribution following his inventions was negative rather than positive. On the advice of his financially astute partner, Matthew Boulton, Watt framed his patents so widely that anyone trying to effect improvements was likely to infringe them. Moreover, he persuaded Parliament to extend his patents of 1769 until 1799, thereby securing a virtual monopoly for Boulton and Watt steam engines for thirty years. With the steam engine the industrial revolution that was to change the face of the world had been launched, and the three decades granted to Boulton and Watt became of supreme importance.

The lives of the pioneers of power production, simple self-taught men without the benefit of academic education, have always elicited a certain amount of romantic admiration. They have often been cited as examples of native genius, working and succeeding in the face of an indifferent scientific 'establishment' which offered them no encouragement. This picture is partly but not quite correct, and rather more will be gained by trying to arrive at an assessment of their achievement that takes into account all the relevant facts. Without doubt Savery, Newcomen and Watt were quite outstanding men who, by personal initiative, remarkable drive and very hard work succeeded in ushering in a new age. However, in their work they were less divorced from the scientific background, which had been created for them by the scholars of the previous generation, than is often assumed.

It has to be remembered that Papin's crucial idea of using steam to create a vacuum was published as early as 1690, when he gave a picture of his experimental arrangement which contains the essential elements used in Newcomen's engine. While there can be no doubt that Newcomen was a blacksmith, it appears that before even beginning his work he obtained advice from the Royal Society's secretary, Robert Hooke, on the principle and operation of Papin's engine. Savery evidently knew about a device for raising water by fire that had been demonstrated by the Marquess of Worcester, and mentioned by the latter in 1663. How exactly this machine worked is not clear, but Cosimo de Medici recorded that he had seen it at Vauxhall, and Savery must also have known Papin's publication since he was in close contact with the Royal Society at the time. James Watt, finally, was in closest touch with academic science from the very beginning of his career, which he started as an instrument maker. The professor of natural philosophy at Glasgow advised the young man to study for a year in London, where he must also have come in contact with scientific circles. Back at Glasgow, Watt discussed his problems with the professor of chemistry, Joseph Black, one of the most outstanding authorities on the theory of heat, and he himself stated that Black explained to him 'his doctrine of latent heat which he had taught for some time'. Watt's closest friend at that time was John Robison, who later became professor of natural philosophy at Edinburgh, and Watt himself was elected to the Royal Society in 1785.

We mention these facts not to detract from the achievements of these pioneers, but to show that their work was inspired throughout by the results of academic scientists with whom they had close contact. The great merit of Savery, Newcomen and Watt was that they put into practice the ideas of the natural philosophers, a task which involved developing new techniques, working with new materials, and using great determination throughout. However, they could never have succeeded or even started their work but for the studies of Guericke, Boyle, Hooke and Papin. The industrial revolution was not hatched in the workshops of artisans but in the meetings of learned societies.

The first application of power producing engines was in a rather restricted and specialized field, the pumping of water from mines, and it was not so much the need for a new power source as their unique suitability for the job that led to the construction of Savery's and Newcomen's engines. Coal and iron were to become the backbone of the industrial revolution, and one of the reason's for England's pre-eminence in this endeavour was her scarcity of wood. Both as fuel and building material, wood retained its use much longer in well-forested countries, and it is significant that in 1845 England was mining seven times as much coal as France. Fifty years earlier coal and the steam engine had found their most important use – as the power source for the manufacture of goods.

Restrictive practices always tend to work against those who institute them. One of the most desirable products which overseas trade had made available was cotton cloth from India, and the wool traders in Europe succeeded in getting this – from their point of view undesirable – influx curtailed. However, they could not stop the importation of raw cotton, especially when the American colonies began to grow it in large quantity. Now cotton could be spun, woven and sold as cloth in England, and demand was fast outstripping productive capacity. Mass manufacture instead of hand-made cloth was the obvious answer, and the machines invented by Hargreaves and Arkwright produced cloth in large quantity and a saving of labour. However, the spinning jennies and the looms had to be powered, and it was then that the streams of Lancashire and Yorkshire began to provide the water power needed to drive the cotton 'mills'. Soon water power became scarce, too, and there was a curious period when steam engines had to be employed to pump water for running over the mill wheels. Instead of grasping the newly harnessed power of heat provided by the steam engine, people frantically tried to replenish with it the dwindling source of water power.

This example shows that the operation of natural philosophy is not bound to a specific need which has to be fulfilled. Like other human activities, it has a life of its own and creates its own laws. Power production, which was to advance Western domination as much as overseas exploration, was never developed by European man for that purpose. It grew out of that insatiable curiosity about the phenomena of the external world and the laws that govern them, and could, as we have seen, lie essentially dormant for a whole century before its potential was recognized. Politicians and economists have forever failed to grasp the fact that natural philosophy compels us to discover, quite irrespective of whether or not the discovery will have economic applications.

Science works in a much more subtle way, because material gain follows from the fact that the discoveries are made in a society which has been conditioned to think scientifically. It is not just the method of natural philosophy in itself which has given the West this curious advantage over the rest of the world, but rather the way in which it has shaped its thinking. As the centuries have rolled by, scientific thinking has gradually invaded every aspect of Western education, far beyond the mere teaching of science. Here, more than in any other way, has the West been set apart from the other races of mankind. All it has done has been to follow the path laid out by the new philosophy. Having once accepted this philosophy because of its obvious material usefulness, the white man could not do otherwise than obey its teaching. While it might be possible to regard the scientific development of ocean navigation as a conscious and purposeful device for dominating the world, this cannot possibly be said of power production, which brought with it the industrial revolution. Nevertheless, this turned out the most efficient way of consolidating and extending the white man's empire. Natural philosophy, as has been pointed out, confers a unique economy of effort, and whichever way the whites applied it, they were simply bound to win – whether they intended to or not.

Steam-driven cotton mills stood at the dawn of the industrial revolution, but they brought with them immense fortunes in overseas trade

車輪舸圖

Fig. 13: Other cultures never developed power production. Although the Chinese invented paddle-wheel vessels long before, these were driven by men working treadmills.

which provided the capital for making more fortunes. In the seventy years before 1835, England's import of raw cotton increased a hundredfold and by then she sold 60 per cent of the world's cotton textiles, France being next with a mere 16 per cent. However, textiles were only the beginning; the real business came from the machines which made machines, including railways and ships. The first steamboat was operating on the Forth and Clyde canal in 1802, and twenty years later a steamer first crossed the Atlantic. All these early craft were propelled by paddle-wheels which, however, were not a Western invention. As early as the fifth century AD the Chinese introduced paddle-wheels for ships, but they operated by treadmill inside the vessel, a system that was retained unchanged until the middle of the nineteenth century when it was still used on the Pearl River during the opium war. In fact, none of the other civilizations ever developed power production until it was introduced by the West.

Watt's steam engine soon became the work horse of Western manufacture and transport, enabling man to command all the tasks which the horse could never have performed. It was James Watt himself who introduced the term 'horsepower' to measure the working capacity of the engines which he sold. In the beginning nobody had seriously considered the amount of coal required by the early engines that pumped water from mines. It was a convenient method to get the water out, and cheaper than any other. However, as more of these pumps were installed people began to count the cost, and the great advantage of Watt's improvements was the saving of fuel. For the first time the efficiency of the heat engine became the most relevant factor. On the industrial bill coal was the most important item, and what mattered was not just the fact that coal could be turned into work, but how many horsepower a given rate of coal consumption would provide. People for the first time were beginning to pay for an entirely new commodity which as yet had not even been fully understood. The physical quantity called 'energy' was not yet recognized and still awaited definition.

When the Aztecs were astounded at the Spaniards' overpowering desire for gold, a substance that was useless either for tools or as an article of diet, Cortés informed them that the white man suffered from a malady of the heart for which gold was the only remedy. Now, well over 400 years later, the white man's hunger for gold has not entirely been stilled, but it has fallen far behind his new appetite for coal, oil and uranium. Less than a century ago, the nomads herding their camels in the Arabian desert had even less use for the crude oil under their feet than the Aztecs had for gold. Gold at least could be turned into jewellery, but there was no use whatever for the Bedouin in the sticky filth – and neither is there today; their camels have not learned either to eat or to drink it. It is food only for the technology of the Westerners who discovered it and developed means of extracting it, but, by the grace of Allah, it can be sold. Energy rather than gold has become the life-blood of Western civilization since the onset of the industrial revolution 250 years ago. The ingredients of this life-blood are all fuels to drive the heat engines. With the advent of the steam engine the study of heat and its transformation into mechanical energy became the economically most important branch of natural philosophy.

The nature of heat had been a source of speculation since antiquity, and the great diversity of its manifestation presented much difficulty in explaining or measuring it. Heat appears in the warmth of the human body, in the elusive flicker of a flame, in the grinding of a wheel against a badly greased axle, and in the rays of the sun; it is a sensation experienced by our skin. This, as Max Planck pointed out in the first paragraph of his *Thermodynamik*, the most famous textbook on the theory of heat, is not a phenomenon that lends itself to quantitative measurement; other physical properties changing with heat have to be employed for this purpose. Evidently Galileo had come to this conclusion three hundred years earlier when he made use of the expansion of air to construct the first thermometer. Other thermometers based on the expansion of liquids soon followed, and have remained essentially unchanged to our day. In this way we have a measure of how much hotter or how much colder, and the concept of a degree of hotness or coldness has been introduced which we call temperature.

All that was now needed was a unit, and here the same international confusion occurred as in the case of the cubit, the yard and the metre; the Germans adopted the French Réaumur scale, the British that of the German Fahrenheit, and the French took after the Swede Celsius. That, in the end, became the scale adopted by scientists, and it simply consists in marking the thermometer once when it is held in melting ice and marking it again in boiling water. Dividing the space between the two marks into one hundred equal intervals, we call each of them one degree centigrade.

There is one refinement to this exercise which is only introduced here because it will become useful a little later. Guillaume Amontons, a contemporary of Boyle and Hooke, studied the expansion of air when heated and found that the volume changed by about one third of 1 per

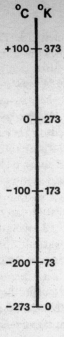

°C °K

+100 — 373

0 — 273

−100 — 173

−200 — 73

−273 — 0

Fig. 14. The centigrade and the Kelvin scales of temperature. For calculating the efficiency of heat engines and many other scientific purposes, the temperature scale introduced by Kelvin, which starts at absolute zero and has no negative values, has many advantages.

cent for each centigrade. Air similarly contracts on cooling, and Amontons concluded that there must exist a temperature at which its volume becomes zero and, since there clearly cannot exist a negative volume, this must be the lowest possible temperature. In this he was right, and today we know that such an 'absolute zero' of temperature does indeed exist at −273° C. For the scientist a zero point provided unambiguously by nature has a great advantage over those chosen arbitrarily, such as freezing or boiling points, and he therefore applies in his work (with profit, as will be seen) the absolute temperature scale. In other words, scientists count in the 'absolute' scale in centigrades from −273° C upwards.

Nevertheless, with a measure of temperature quantitatively established only half the task was accomplished. When one wants to calculate the power derived from water driving a mill wheel, two things have to be known: one is the height from which the water runs down, and the other is the quantity of water running through the mill channel. Trying to compare the water mill with a heat engine, the temperature will give us the height but we still lack a measure for the quantity of heat. Heat, as Hooke suspected, is vested in the vibration of the smallest particles of matter, in its atoms and molecules, and trying to measure the amount of such vibration of invisible particles appears a hopeless task. The problem was solved in a most ingenious way, which shows the immense flexibility of natural philosophy in arriving at the required result.

Even the Greeks knew that when a hot and a cold object are brought into contact with each other, the hot one will get colder and the cold one warmer until both have the same temperature. They concluded that something had flowed from the hot to the cold body, a concept that was held throughout the Middle Ages and also by the other great civilizations. The great step beyond this idea, taken by Western science, was to measure this 'something'. To do this, the something had to be defined, and it is significant that the practitioners of natural philosophy did not wait for an interpretation of the nature of heat as molecular motion. Instead they invented a hypothetical substance representing heat which they called 'caloric', and to which they simply gave all the attributes that were needed to explain the observed phenomena. Most scientists were reasonably satisfied that caloric did not actually exist, but it allowed them a make-believe world in which they could do what they wanted to do badly; to measure quantities of heat.

Caloric was defined as a weightless substance, dissolved in matter, which would flow from a warm object to a cold one when they came into contact. All substances were assumed to contain caloric, and the concentration of caloric in a body was supposed to be indicated by its temperature. It had been shown that the flow of caloric was not accompanied by a weight change, but this did not matter in the case of a hypothetical substance. Measurements of a quantity of heat now proceeded in strict analogy with mechanical principles. The unit of mechanical work is defined as the effort of lifting one gram by one centimetre. The unit of caloric was accordingly defined as raising the temperature of one gram of water by one degree, and it was called a 'calorie'. By laying down a quantitative measure for an amount of heat, the way was opened for a new scientific method called 'thermodynamics'.

It proved successful beyond all expectation. Its strength lies in its complete independence of the nature of the substance involved, and of the kind of process treated. Its validity is universal, its application unlimited, and its results always strictly correct. The quantities used for the computations are always measurable, such as temperature, pressure or volume, and no detailed theory involving assumptions is ever used in the operations of thermodynamics. Although the primary aim in developing it was an assessment of the operation of heat engines, thermodynamics has since been applied successfully to a host of quite different problems, such as the functioning of a chemical factory, an electric battery, an oil refinery, and the human body.

The man who laid the foundation of this immensely powerful scientific method was a young French engineering officer called Sadi Carnot. When he died at the age of thirty-six of cholera he had already published his famous treatise *Réflexions sur la puissance motrice du feu et sur les machines propres a développer cette puissance* (*On the Motive Power of Heat and on Machines Designed to Develop This Power*). This article, written at the age of twenty-seven, contains a mere sketch of Carnot's ideas, but fortunately his notes were saved and subsequently published in 1878, forty-six years after his death, by his younger brother. They show that Carnot had developed thermodynamics into a fully self-consistent method, anticipating largely the ideas of Mayer, Joule and Helmholtz, who are generally credited with the principle of conservation of energy.

James Watt had made his fortune by building steam engines which were vastly more efficient in fuel consumption than those made by his predecessors. His improvements were based on an astute understanding, from the practical point of view, of the basic principles underlying the functioning of steam engines. This, however, could not lead to a quantitative assessment of the process itself. While Watt's approach was eminently successful in satisfying the immediate need for better machines, he could not guess from it the value of their ultimate efficiency, nor appreciate the factors responsible for it. This is best shown by his reluctance to use high steam pressure which, he felt, involved safety risks. Carnot's theoretical analysis, on the other hand, showed that this was to be the one road to higher efficiency.

Carnot's engineering training was highly mathematical; his father, too, had been a noted mathematician. Instead of following, like Papin and the other inventors, the road that led to the industrial revolution, Carnot used the generalized methods of Newton and Boyle. The original power source of the industrial revolution had been the streams of Lancashire. Their mechanical power was given by the amount of water flowing through the mill and the difference in the height of the water level. In strict analogy with this mechanical example, Carnot treated the steam engine that had replaced the water mill as a device which delivered power because caloric was flowing through it from a higher to a lower level of temperature. He constructed the theoretical cycle of operation which made his name immortal, and which was so universal in its applicability that it can be turned to the interpretation of any heat engine, irrespective of its construction or working principle.

The result of Carnot's mathematical exercise was most surprising. The power that can be delivered by the water mill simply depends on the height by which the water has dropped. In the heat engine this is not so. Its power does not simply depend on the drop in the temperature, but on this drop divided by the absolute temperature. It will be remembered that this absolute temperature is counted in centigrades from $-273°$ C. This means that, unlike a mechanical device, a heat engine can never be made to approach 100 per cent efficiency. For instance, it has sometimes been suggested that all our energy requirements would be satisfied if only we could build a machine that abstracts heat from the ocean, cooling its surface by just one degree. As a matter of fact such an engine is well within the realm of possibility, but it would not help us very much. Since the absolute temperature of the ocean is about $300°$, the temperature drop of one degree will result in a maximum efficiency of $1/300$, only one third of one per cent. Thus Carnot showed that in any heat engine a large part of the caloric flowing through the engine can never be transformed into useful work, but has to be discarded as waste heat at a lower temperature. His study also indicated clearly what factors had to be taken into account in order to build an efficient heat engine, and that the relatively low efficiency of any heat engine is due to a fundamental law of nature which cannot be overcome by clever design. Since practically all our power production, including that from nuclear reactors, is ultimately based on heat engines, Carnot's principle, unwelcome as it may be, represents the fundamental law which has to be taken into account when trying to still our hunger for energy.

The Carnots were an illustrious family. Sadi's nephew, the son of his younger brother who had published Sadi's scientific papers, became President of France. His father, Lazare Carnot, has gone down in French history as the 'organizer of victory' – of the revolutionary armies. A captain under Louis XVI, Lazare Carnot espoused the cause of the revolution, becoming a staunch republican who voted for the death of the king. He was an expert on military engineering who combined scientific training with strategic genius, and the defeat of France's external enemies during the troubled years of the National Convention was largely due to Carnot's superb planning. Having been a close colleague of Robespierre, he not only avoided the latter's fate but became one of the five members of the all-powerful Directorate of 1795. Although not in sympathy with Napoleon's strategy of global conquest, Carnot served the French armies as their supreme organizer down to the Hundred Days. Banished under the second restoration, he died in

1823 at Magdeburg, but was eventually buried in the Pantheon in 1889.

Sadi Carnot owed much to the inspiration provided by his father – not as a general but as a mathematician. Lazare Carnot had been one of the founders of an educational institution which was to become a major weapon in the white man's armoury for the conquest of the world. This was the establishment of the École Polytechnique at Paris in 1795. This unique institution was a true child of the young revolution, purposely designed to give fullest scope to the scientific genius that had languished under the rule of the aristocracy. The revolution was a creation of the bourgeoisie and the scholars and scientists were, on the whole, its intellectual vanguard. In keeping with the turbulent times of its origin, the École Polytechnique was primarily devoted to military engineering, but civil engineering projects also figured conspicuously in its curriculum. Whereas the object of the learned societies of the seventeenth century had been the discovery of the laws of nature, with their application as a secondary pursuit, the École Polytechnique was established with the conscious aim of using the laws of science in order to harness the powers of nature for man's benefit.

It is significant that the French scholars regarded mathematics as the basis of the practical exploitation of natural phenomena. Probably the first conscious analysis of the meaning of natural philosophy was in regarding mathematical connexion of observed fact as the essence of scientific progress. Admittedly, mathematics had been used in the interpretation of natural events since Galileo and Newton, but the École Polytechnique provided the first instance of making mathematical training the foundation of a practical exploitation of natural forces. In due course similar institutions in other countries were to follow the lead of the French revolutionaries. The technical high schools of Germany, Switzerland, and then of America, became the breeding places for that new species of academically trained engineer on whom the Western world became completely dependent for its chemical, electrical and transport industries. The pattern set by the French prototype left no doubt about the inspired vision of its founders. The motto of the École Polytechnique from its beginning was 'nothing but the best will do', and it is reflected in the choice of its teaching staff. The eminent mathematician Lagrange, who had filled Euler's place at the Prussian Academy of Sciences in Berlin, was called back to France by Louis XVI after the death of Frederick the Great, and then, honoured by the Revolution, he became professor at the École Polytechnique. His colleagues there were Laplace and Fourier, both in turn presidents of the École. Another professor was Lazare Carnot. His son was not only the first man to implement the mathematical teaching of the École Polytechnique in the field of fundamental engineering, but also emphasized with his brilliant work the basis of natural philosophy: economy of effort.

When James Watt coined the word 'horsepower' as the unit of the new currency of the industrial revolution, neither he nor his contemporaries knew what exactly they were charging the 'money' for. It took another half century for people to discover the true definition of the commodity they were producing, selling and buying. This, of course, is not too surprising when we consider that a manufacturer had to buy raw cotton and coal, burn the latter, and end up with a length of cotton cloth. He also had to pay his workers, including those who manned the steam engines, which also had to be paid for. It was a bit easier in the case of the railway magnates, who also had to buy and burn coal in order to convey passengers and goods formerly drawn by horses. When pulling a cart, the horse performs 'work' which, in this case, is expressed as exerting its force over a distance. That, indeed, is the accepted and correct physical definition, and the rate at which a horse does the work is the 'horsepower'. This formulation is a purely mechanical one as, for instance, the compression of a spring; but then, the spring can be released at some future time and will deliver at its extension the work that had been put into it. In other words, the quantity which we have called work can lie dormant without being apparent.

Things become even more complex when a cannon ball is fired. Its mass is moved over a large distance, and so the work is quite apparent. But where was it stored? Clearly it must have been hidden in the gunpowder before that was ignited. The fact that work can be hidden was already implicit in Galileo's experiment when he let a ball run down an inclined plane, only to rise to the same height on an opposed inclined plane. There was nothing about the ball, before it was released, to show that in rolling down it was capable of performing work. And there was nothing after it had ascended the opposing plane to show that it had performed work. Leibniz, in 1695, had called the motion of the ball its *vis viva*, its living force, and he as well as Newton was fully aware that this work could be stored. As long as only mechanical processes are involved such formulations are sufficient, but storage of work in gunpowder requires other assumptions. There a chemical explosion had been transformed into mechanical motion. Even in the apparently simple case of the horse, its fodder and the air it breathes had been mysteriously changed into mechanical work. It gradually became apparent that there must exist a physical quantity that can assume many guises, often completely hidden, but which may, under certain circumstances, be transformed into mechanical work. And mechanical work is the coin in which man has to make use of this hidden treasure.

In 1807 Thomas Young gave a name to this quantity; he called it 'energy'. Young was a physicist whose best known work was in the field of optics, but he also practised as a physician. In addition, he was a classics scholar who, at the same time as Champollion, deciphered the Egyptian hieroglyphs. It was his classics training that led him to describe this new universal quantity as vested *en ergon*, i.e. 'in work'. Soon investigation of the energy concept became the foremost task of natural philosophy, and its most useful means of describing natural phenomena. The inventions of the past centuries and their use for the exploitation of the forces of nature were relegated to second place in comparison with the all-embracing energy concept, for this turned out to be the basis of all of them. The recognition of energy and its universal significance has to be rated as one of the most important steps in the white race's progress towards world domination. It provided much more than just a new technological currency; it enhanced enormously the power of prediction which is the essence of success of natural philosophy.

Although Sadi Carnot, in his mathematical analysis of the efficiency of heat engines, used the old concept of caloric, this had by then become nothing more than a convenient calculating aid which did not affect in the least the value of his conclusions. On the other hand, he forged a connection between heat and the *puissance motrice*, the motive power into which heat could be converted. In fact the energy concept, irrespective of the name he gave it, was responsible for the success of the new method of thermodynamics which he had created. The astonishing universality of its application is simply the result of the universal nature of energy.

Doubts on the material nature of heat had been raised by Robert Hooke and many others. One of these was Benjamin Thompson, a British Tory born in Massachusetts in 1753, and better known under his Bavarian title of Count Rumford. He was a most gifted man and a colourful personality. At the age of nineteen he had married a wealthy widow whose status and fortune brought him into contact with the influential circles of the colony. Later, his keen observational powers and his inventiveness were demonstrated when, as a British spy, he wrote his reports in invisible ink. Then, however, the success of the American troops forced Thompson to go to England where he soon obtained a high government position, was knighted by George III, and elected into the Royal Society in 1781. This honour was awarded in recognition of Thompson's scientific work on ballistics, in the course of which he also became interested in the nature of heat since this was responsible for the motion of the projectile.

It was this success in military engineering which induced the Elector Karl Theodor of Bavaria to attract Thompson to his court. Here he not only continued his scientific work, but also introduced numerous innovations into the economy of the country, all of which were prompted by a scientific assessment of the people's needs. In one day he had no less than 2,600 layabouts arrested and set to work in a factory estate prepared for them. His argument was: 'To make vicious and abandoned people happy, it has generally been supposed necessary first to make them virtuous. But why not reverse this order? Why not make them happy, and then virtuous?' He also devised the recipe for an inexpensive but nutritious broth, and to this day many Continental menus feature 'Rumford soup'. In recognition of these multifarious services, the Elector had Thompson created a Count of the Holy Roman Empire, who chose for his title the little town of Rumford in Massachusetts, which after the American victory had been renamed Concord. Two years later, in 1795, the Elector had to flee before the onslaught of the French and Austrian armies. Although Rumford played an important part in the successful defence of Munich, his social measures had not earned him the gratitude of the Bavarians, and he settled in London.

There he concerned himself with smoke abatement and the re-design of domestic fireplaces. Together with Joseph Banks, the president of the Royal Society, Rumford laid plans for an establishment similar to the École Polytechnique which had just been founded in Paris. Both men were convinced of the need to create a practical engineering school in England, and in 1800 they obtained from George III the charter for the Royal Institution. However, social conditions in England were quite different from those in revolutionary France. The aristocracy and not the intellectuals were represented in the management of the new foundation, and the engineering school's place was taken by lectures addressed to the informed nobility. Nevertheless, Rumford had chosen Humphry Davy as scientific director, and he and his successors – Thomas Young, Michael Faraday and James Dewar – brought immense fame to the Institution. Rumford, however, was so disenchanted with the metamorphosis of his idea that he went to live in France, where he was received enthusiastically. But his last years, spent in Paris, were not to be happy ones. He quarrelled with both Lagrange and Laplace, and his marriage to another wealthy woman, the widow of the celebrated Lavoisier who had been executed in the Revolution, proved disastrous.

In 1798 Rumford had submitted to the Royal Society his most important contribution, the *Enquiry concerning the Sources of Heat which is excited by Friction*. The observations on which it is founded were made when he supervised the boring of cannon for the Elector of Bavaria. He had noticed that, particularly when the boring tool was blunt, both the gun barrel and the chippings became very hot, showing that the mechanical energy of the drill had been partly changed into heat. From this Rumford concluded that heat must be a form of energy, and not a fluid such as caloric. Although the actual nature of heat as molecular motion was of great scientific importance, its practical application as a form of energy was really what mattered. It was this aspect that was used twenty-five years later by Sadi Carnot as the basis on which he developed thermodynamics. What still remained to be established was the quantitative relation between heat and mechanical energy.

This work, which led to the fundamental law of conservation of energy, was undertaken quite independently by three men: Robert Mayer, James Prescott Joule and Hermann von Helmholtz. The conservation of mechanical energy had already been suggested by Galileo's experiment with the inclined planes. It was noted that by minimizing friction the motion of the rolling ball, like that of a swinging pendulum, could be kept up for longer and longer times. Newton's laws of mechanics, and their application to the undiminishing rotation of moon and planets, left little doubt that their energy of motion was conserved. However, the full significance of this fact was only realized when it became clear that mechanical energy could be converted into heat, as in Rumford's experiments, or heat converted into energy, as shown by the steam engine. To this had to be added the chemical energy firing the cannon ball, and soon also the energy of electricity and magnetism. In fact, it was this convertibility of quite different forces of nature into each other which led to the concept of energy as a universal physical quantity. All that now remained to be done was to show that, in all these transformations of one energy form into another, nothing was left over. This is not the place to go into the ingenious ways by which this was proved. It suffices to say that by the middle of the nineteenth century all scientists were convinced that energy can neither be created nor destroyed.

From the very beginning, natural philosophers have set themselves two tasks. The first is to discover by experiment new phenomena, and the second is to correlate these observations into a coherent body of knowledge. The true landmarks in this quest are those stages at which it suddenly became possible to combine previously unrelated facts or laws into a much grander universal scheme. In this synthesis the recognition of energy as a physical quantity of paramount importance is outstanding, because the feature of its conservation in *any* process links up our observations in mechanics, heat, optics, electricity, magnetism and chemistry. Moreover, this all-embracing combination of natural phenomena is of a strictly quantitative nature, and allows a width of accurate calculation far beyond anything that was feasible before. It permits us to express the energy of a falling stone in calories, the force of an explosion in electrical units, and the illumination of a room in mechanical measure. The notion of energy and its conservation gave Western man not only a new aspect of the world but also forced him into a new way of thinking.

The white man's intellectual departure from the rest of the world had begun four centuries ago when, compelled by an unexplained impulse, he set out to explore the world around him. In some cases, as for instance in setting up the Sagres research establishment, this departure was abrupt; but in many other respects it was a gradual rather than a sudden parting of the ways. The West built better ships and forged more effective arms than the other great civilizations but, if they had really wanted to, the others too could have done the same. For although the change in Western thought had been fundamental, the whites had as yet done nothing which could not be understood by the other races. Power production, even if they could not have developed it, was of course not beyond their comprehension, but they could never have formulated the concept of energy. It was a creation of Western thought for which the others utterly lacked the basis. Energy, its conservation, and the usefulness of the notion of conservation, were ideas that had grown out of more than two centuries of natural philosophy. And this was a field of development in which none but the white man had participated. He had not withheld his ideas from others; they just were not interested, because the white man's way of thinking was alien and seemed of little meaning to them.

Now the gap had grown so wide that any understanding which could bridge it had to be on the white man's terms. The belated attempts of the rest of the world to catch up with Western progress entailed its intellectual enslavement. Participation in the Westerners' high standard of living presupposed operation of natural philosophy, and this had to be learned from the whites. The other races had no option but to imitate

Western methods, since they had nothing of their own to offer to the world of technological progress and success. Largely by their own choice, and certainly by their own default, they became economically second-class citizens of the world. Thus the white man's domination was not primarily due to his cruelty or his aggressiveness, but to the long and patient development of his own natural philosophy.

CHAPTER SIX

Electromagnetism, the silent giant

When the Portuguese navigators of the Renaissance set out on the exploration of the uncharted oceans, they were greatly aided by a Chinese invention: the mariner's compass. Without it their quest would have been immeasurably more difficult, or perhaps even impossible. The use of the magnetic needle had been introduced into Europe late in the twelfth century, probably through Arab seafarers, but it is known to have been used about two centuries earlier in Chinese ships. In fact, the Chinese had known and made use of the directional power of the lodestones many centuries earlier – but only on land. Their Taoist philosophy taught them to live in harmony with the forces of nature, and lodestones played an important part in geomancy, which was used to decide where to build one's house or one's tomb. In any case, overseas exploration of other countries was alien to their basic principles. For thousands of years the children of Han had been convinced that they were the only civilized race, and that they lived at the centre of the world, the Middle Kingdom Chung-guo, a name which has been retained by them to this day. They were surrounded by barbarians, against whom they protected themselves with the Great Wall, and they were confident that nothing could be learned by visiting other peoples. Thus to make overseas voyages for subjugating or even conquering them was clearly too preposterous to be contemplated. It was left to the West to use the compass for this purpose.

Magnetism had in fact been known to the Greeks, and in the sixth century BC Thales of Miletus mentions the fact that bits of a certain stone would attract each other. Lucretius, 600 years later, mentions the attraction of iron by a stone found near the city of Magnesia in Thessaly, from which the phenomenon of magnetism derived its name. Lucretius also mentions magnetic repulsion when he writes: 'Sometimes, too, iron draws back from this stone; for it is wont to flee from and follow it in

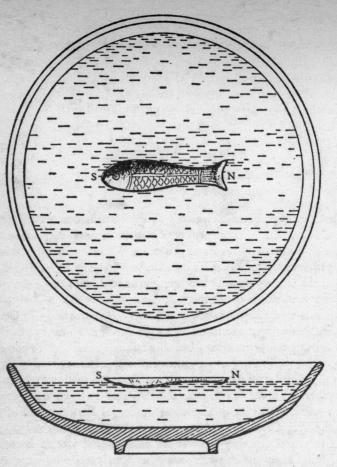

Fig. 15. The magnetic compass was invented by the Chinese, who mainly used it for geomancy and divination before introducing it as a navigational aid. Its simplest form consisted of a wooden fish containing the magnet, which was floated in a shallow dish of water.

turn.' Clearly, magnetism was a complex and puzzling aspect of nature, and it is not surprising that for a long time it received little attention, save for its use in the compass. Not till 1600 was it investigated more thoroughly – by Queen Elizabeth's court physician, William Gilbert, who published his famous treatise *De Magnete* in that year.

Magnetism had been known since antiquity as an out of the way, 'fringe' feature of matter, and the same was true for electricity. This name, given to it by Gilbert, is derived from the Greek word for amber since it had been noted that this fossil resin, when rubbed, could attract small, light particles such as seeds or bits of fluff. The Chinese, too, had made a similar observation in about 500 AD when they mentioned this feature as a means of testing genuine amber. Their only other reference to electricity appears to be a mention, five centuries earlier, of the phenomenon of sparks appearing when hair is combed. We cannot possibly attempt in this book to trace in any detail the long story of the discovery and application of electromagnetism from the time of the Renaissance onwards. Our only object will be to show how the mind of Western man coped with this immense and extremely difficult task – starting from essentially nothing.

As in the case of gravitation, the modern user of electrical appliances cannot be aware of the forbidding intellectual hurdles that stood in the way before a few spurious and not easily reproducible observations could be turned into electric technology. It seems quite inconceivable that, only two hundred years ago, our knowledge of electricity was still based on glass rods rubbed with catskin, and that people alive today can remember the first electric light in the shops and homes of capital cities. The mental breakthrough required in scientific thinking was profound, because nature had not only failed to provide copious phenomena to go on with, but even these were tenuous and often contradictory. She had laid on no more than one grand display of this normally hidden force in the form of thunderstorms which, moreover, went unheeded. In a little book on natural phenomena written in the eighteenth century by a member of Magdalen Hall, Oxford, and intended to provide subjects for 'polite conversation', thunderstorms are described as collisions of 'nitrous and sulphurous clouds'. The author was clearly not inclined to invoke a rare fringe phenomenon like electricity to explain lightning.

The difficulty in understanding gravity had arisen from the fact that the force itself is too weak to demonstrate its attraction in the laboratory, but that it is all-important to us because we are so close to a very great mass, the earth. On the other hand, the forces of electricity and magnetism can easily be observed in the mutual interaction of magnet needles, or in the attraction and repulsion of pith balls. These forces are, in fact, vastly (10^{27} times) stronger than gravity, but their action in the experiments just mentioned is extremely small; nothing like that of a boulder rolling down a mountain side under gravity. The next hurdle in understanding was that, unlike gravity, electricity and magnetism show not only attraction but also repulsion. To make matters worse, the experimenters soon noticed that whereas in a magnet the north pole is always paired with an equally strong south pole, a positive or negative electric charge can apparently exist by itself. Furthermore, a piece of iron which was not magnetic could be made so by being stroked with a magnet, but the trouble with electrical observations was that exactly the same experiment would work on one day and not on another, particularly when it rained.

These, then, were the difficulties confronting the natural philosophers when they tried to elucidate the hidden forces that rule our lives as influentially as gravity. They had started with nothing, only to discover an enormous variety of confusing and contradictory features that opened up a new aspect of our physical world – but not a simple one, at least as yet. Nevertheless, true to its pattern, the exploratory spirit of the white race persisted, not only tenaciously but with exactly the same method that had proved so successful in the past. However discouraging the results might be, they only stimulated more curiosity, and the scientists simply went on experimenting until the results began to make sense.

The first step, therefore, was to produce the phenomenon to be investigated, in sizeable quantity, and it was again the enterprising and wealthy burgomaster of Magdeburg, Otto von Guericke, who took the lead. In 1663, instead of rubbing small pieces of amber, he designed and operated a machine for doing the job. It consisted of a big sphere of sulphur, rotated by a winch, on which the hand was placed. Isaac Newton replaced the sulphur by a glass globe, and from then on a great number of various friction machines were invented which produced electricity reliably and in sufficient quantity to supply not only shocks but even sparks. At first the electric shock and the length of the spark, neither of which could be measured all that well, served as indicators for the electric 'charge'. William Gilbert had already used a rough indicator that relied on electric attraction and repulsion, and this was now developed into a measuring instrument, called the electroscope.

With friction machines to produce electricity, and the electroscope to measure it, the scene was set for systematic investigation. Now the first significant results began to be obtained. In 1729 Stephen Gray made an experiment that immediately produced two important discoveries. He showed that electricity could pass along 800 feet of wet hempen cord hung up in his garden on silk threads, thereby discovering the phenomenon of the electric current and also showing that, while the cord was a conductor, silk was an insulator. Further investigation soon showed that while the wet string was indeed a conductor, it was a very poor one when compared with metal wires, whereas non-metals such as glass,

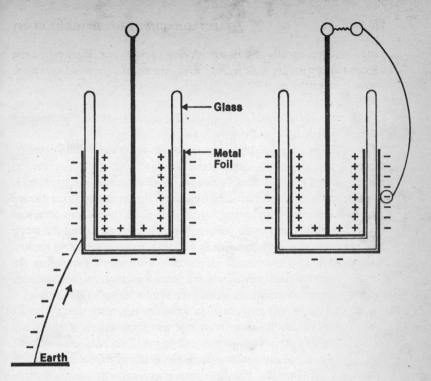

Fig. 16. Although the electromagnetic forces are immensely stronger than the force of gravity they are rarely apparent. The reason for this is their polarity, which allows positive and negative charges to 'pair off', thereby presenting an overall aspect of neutrality. The Leyden jar shows how paired charges can be stored but remain hidden.

porcelain or sulphur were definitely insulators. The first step towards an electro-technology was thereby taken.

In 1746 P. van Musschenbroek in Leyden invented a storage device for electricity, the famous Leyden jar. It consisted of an insulating glass jar, covered inside and out with metal foil. When the inner layer was connected to an electric machine, and the outer layer to the earth, very strong charges built up between these two metal foils. This was not only a convenient storage for electricity, but it also showed that there must exist two kinds of electricity, positive and negative. If the interior was charged positively, negative electricity ran up from the ground to the outside, binding by mutual attraction the positive charge inside. Nothing of this stored electricity could be seen; the appearance of the Leyden jar remaining unchanged. However, when wires connected to the inside and outside of the jar respectively were now brought close together, the two kinds of electricity would combine in a strong spark.

Apart from being a useful and instructive device, the Leyden jar teaches an important lesson, the full meaning of which was not understood until some time later. When either a positively or a negatively charged body is approached by an electrical indicator, the indicator will show a reading which is proportional to the strength of the charge. No such indication will be observed when we approach a Leyden jar, although it may hold a charge a thousand times stronger. The reason for this is that in the Leyden jar the charges are 'bound' to each other, a fact which completely cancels their outward effect. Unlike gravity, the electromagnetic forces have polarity which, in spite of their enormous strength, tends to keep them hidden by being paired off. Gravity cannot pair because it is always attractive, and thus cannot hide its effect. Whereas, in a fashion quite similar to the case of electric charges, north and south magnetic poles in, let us say, two bar magnets, lying side by side, will have hardly any effect on their environment. The discovery of this gigantic hidden force that surrounds us unseen was a major triumph of Western natural philosophy. It was to be followed in our day by the discovery of another invisible force, many million times stronger.

Even before Newton formulated his theory of gravitational attraction, the behaviour of magnets had elicited particular interest because it involved action at a distance. Magnets were able to affect magnetic needles without touching them, and when vacuum pumps became available it was soon found that the air of the atmosphere had no part in this transmission of magnetism. When William Gilbert investigated this action systematically, he observed that magnet needles, suspended in the vicinity of a lodestone, would take up definite directions along magnetic 'lines of force'. He thus showed that the space around a magnet had certain properties which, while invisible, were capable of influencing other magnets. We nowadays refer to these properties as a magnetic 'field of force', in the same way as we talk about electric or gravitational fields of force. It is a form of description which has been found extremely useful in theoretical as well as in practical calculation, without requiring any philosophical interpretation of its deeper meaning. We will accept it and use it in the following pages without speculating on its fundamental aspects.

Once it was realized that there exists electric and magnetic action at a distance, in the same manner as the force of gravity, the question arose whether electric and magnetic forces also decrease in strength with the

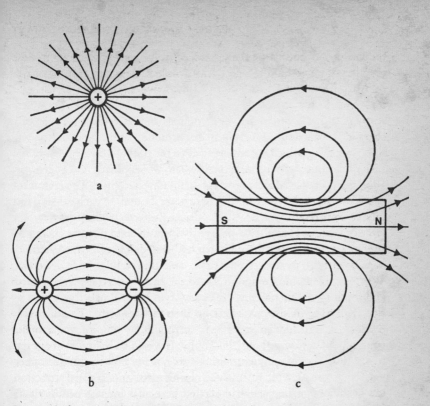

Fig. 17. *The force exerted by an isolated positive charge radiates evenly in all directions (a). When a positive and negative charge are brought close together, the 'lines of force' join up, demonstrating the pairing off (b). A similar pattern (c) is shown by the lines of force emanating from a bar magnet. However, isolated north or south magnetic poles have never been observed.*

square of the distance. From various experiments this seemed probable, and the inverse square law for both a magnetic pole and an electric charge was elegantly demonstrated in 1784 by Charles Augustin de Coulomb.

The fact that the forces of gravity, electricity and magnetism all obey exactly the same general law is not really astonishing, since this law is a simple property of our three-dimensional space. In this space anything emanating from one point and equally in all directions has to weaken in the inverse square of the distance from this point. Take as an example the quantity of light, coming from a point source, which passes through a frame of 1 square inch, held at 1 foot distance from the source. Then,

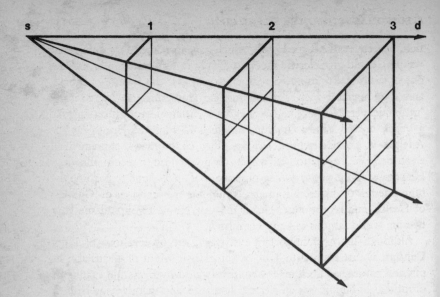

Fig. 18. The 'inverse square law' of gravitational and electromagnetic forces is a necessary feature of three-dimensional space. The diagram shows how any outflow from a source 'S' must thin out according to the square of the distance.

since light travels in straight lines, this same quantity will pass at 2 feet distance through a frame of 4 square inches, at 3 feet through one of 9 square inches, at 4 feet through 16 square inches, and so on. This is a simple geometrical construction showing that, since no light is added or can escape from this cone, the same amount of light has to be spread over an area of 2^2, 3^2 and 4^2 of the original frame as we go, instead of 1 foot, now 2 feet, 3 feet or 4 feet away from the source. It is obvious that the same law must apply to gravity, magnetism and electricity thinning out into space from one source. It is a beautiful example of the simplicity of natural philosophy.

As observations on the effects of electricity and magnetism increased, the idea that they were the results of 'effluvia' begain to gain ground. The concept of such 'effluvia' is not, of course, in contradiction with that of modern field theory, but for a time there was much confusion about the origin of this action at a distance. Not unnaturally it was suspected that electricity might be the enigmatic *vis vitae*, the living force by which life is distinguished from inanimate matter. After all, amber became electrified when rubbed by a warm hand, and it was the friction of the human hand on Guericke's sulphur globe that produced electrification. Moreover, the torpedo fish, which gave its name to the submarine weapon, could give electric shocks sufficient to stun a swimmer. In fact, one of the first actions noted with electricity was this feature of shocks, and soon medical men claimed miracle cures through hypnosis by 'magnetic' personalities like Mesmer, or by using electrification. In 1780 a quack doctor, James Graham, set up a 'Temple of Health' at the Adelphi in London which, among other contraptions, contained an electrified bed, copulation on which was guaranteed to secure offspring. He persuaded the pretty young nursemaid of a colleague to become the high priestess of this establishment, combining the functions of 'Goddess of Health' and receptionist. Her name was Emma Lyon and she later became world famous as Lady Hamilton.

Although the next important discovery, the observations of Luigi Galvani, at first seemed to support the animal origin of electricity, its physical nature had been made abundantly clear by Benjamin Franklin's proof that lightning was an electric discharge, and that damage from it could be avoided by placing a metal conductor in its path. In 1770 Galvani, a physiologist at Bologna, noted that dissected frogs' legs which he had hung up on copper wires twitched when they accidentally touched an iron railing. He also observed this twitching when a Leyden jar was discharged in their vicinity. Alessandro Volta, a physicist of Padua university, at first agreed with Galvani's suggestion that the effect had its origin in the frog's tissue, but then found in a remarkable series of careful experiments that electricity was generated when two metals, in this case iron and copper, were connected by a wet medium, the frog's leg. Next, he omitted the frog's leg altogether, and replaced it with inorganic moisture, finding that zinc and copper were the most effective metals. In 1800 he piled a large number of zinc and copper discs, separated by moist paper, on top of each other, and thus constructed the first electric battery. A momentous breakthrough in electrical investigation had been achieved, ringing in a new century which was to end with electric current as an indispensable adjunct to our technology.

Volta's pile was only the beginning of a truly breathtaking rush of experiments, leading to a host of highly significant results. Whereas up to then research had been limited by friction machines, which produced small quantities of electricity but at unpleasantly high tension, now the galvanic cell provided large quantities of electricity at harmlessly low tension. Batteries delivered remarkably steady currents which enabled the flow of electricity to be studied in detail. Admittedly, nobody knew what electricity was, nor were they to know for another century, but this did not really matter. Scientists had learned by then that laws can always be based on any physical quantities, provided these were properly defined and could be accurately measured. This method had been used again and again in natural philosophy, and had always been found to pay off.

The existence of electric currents had already been demonstrated by Stephen Gray's wet rope seventy years earlier, and now the battery offered a convenient means of investigating their behaviour systematically. Although nobody had much faith in the existence of caloric, this hypothetical weightless fluid had proved most useful for studying the flow of heat by comparing it with the well-known flow of water. Now a new weightless fluid, electricity, was to be treated in exactly the same manner. True to form, the method worked again. As water flows downhill and caloric from hot to cold, so electricity was judged to flow from the positive pole of a battery through any conductor to its negative pole. It will flow so long as the circuit is not broken, and it can be broken and closed by a switch, which corresponds to a water tap. All that the electrical engineer now needed were the equivalents of the height from which the water runs down, the amount of water flowing, and the size of the pipe. He knew that in the case of water these quantities depend upon each other and that, if two of them are known, he could calculate the third.

In electricity the height of fall is called the tension and, in honour of Volta, its unit of measurement is called the *volt*. The rate at which electricity is flowing down under its tension, the current, is named after André-Marie Ampère, whom we will meet presently. Finally, the resistance that a pipe offers to the flow of water is also called resistance in electricity and it is measured in *ohms*, so named after Simon Ohm who, in 1826, framed the law connecting these three quantities. This is simple in the extreme and reads:

$$volts = ampères \times ohms$$

In addition, an electric current represents a flow of energy which can be measured in horsepower. However, in honour of James Watt, who originally expressed the power delivered by his steam engine in these units, a more convenient measure of electric energy flow has been named the *watt*, which is 0·00134 horsepower, and we get:

$$watts = volts \times ampères$$

These two simple equations provide us with all we need to know for most electrical circuits, from operating a torch to wiring up a house, including an electric central heating system. These two little equations have been mentioned to show the immense strength of accurate prediction provided by science. It is utterly reliable and not necessarily complicated.

Carried away by our success in describing electric currents so simply in analogy to the flow of water, we have said nothing so far about their relation to magnetism. That such a relation exists had been suspected from the earliest days of electrical research, but it was only found when the galvanic battery had provided a reliable and easily manageable current supply. With the battery at the scientists' disposal, this basic relation was bound to be discovered soon, and it was now only a question when, where and by whom. Lots of people now looked for it, and the lucky dice were thrown by Hans Christian Oersted, a professor in Copenhagen who had graduated in pharmacy, had presented a doctoral thesis on the philosophy of Immanuel Kant, and had been awarded gold medals for his work in medicine and aesthetics. It was his interest in philosophy that drew him into experimental work on electricity, but in this he was hampered by an excessive lack of manual skill. In one of his experiments he placed a wire carrying a current at right angles over a compass needle. Nothing happened, but after the experiment, and evidently largely by accident, the wire shifted so that it lay parallel to the needle which now showed a strong deflexion. The missing link, the connection between electricity and magnetism, had been discovered.

The course of events following immediately upon Oersted's observation is worth recounting in detail. Oersted's experiments began sometime in July 1820, and his first memorandum is dated on the 21st of that month. Shortly afterwards the French physicist and astronomer François Arago passed through Copenhagen and learned of this result. After his return to Paris, Arago described it before the Académie des Sciences at its session on 11 September. Ampère immediately concluded that, since a current affected a magnet, the current must have produced a magnetic field itself, and another effect was to be expected. An electric current running through a wire should affect another current running independently through a neighbouring wire. He carried out the experiment and reported its success to the Académie on 25 September. Meanwhile, Jean-Baptiste Biot and Félix Savart performed a more sophisticated version of Oersted's experiment, from which they deduced the mathematical relation between current and magnetic field. They reported it to the Académie on 30 October, and it became known as the Biot-Savart law, one of the cornerstones of electromagnetic theory.

Thus, less than two months after Oersted's observation became known, the basis of modern electromagnetism, called the first law of circulation, was established in the form which has remained unchanged to this day. The question that interests us here is, how was it possible? The answer, of course, lies in the fundamental trust of European man in his natural philosophy, his conviction that he could predict any course of events provided that he had been able to express them in the form of strict mathematical laws. It was this basic belief that had created the brilliant French school of mathematicians, whose focal point was the École Polytechnique. Whereas in England the legacy of Newton passed to the practical engineers of the industrial revolution, the French had spent their time in extending Newtonian mechanics, with all its implications, into a strict and highly generalized mathematical system. The efforts of these two great scientific movements complemented each other in the two basic branches of natural philosophy. The British chose empirical experimentation, and the French mathematical analysis. This generalized basis of science had been created by the illustrious professors of the École Polytechnique, D'Alembert, Laplace, Legendre, Lagrange and Fourier, to whose names that of the creator of potential theory, Siméon Denis Poisson, now had to be added. Here lay the secret of the miracle of September–October 1820. The mathematical establishment of the École Polytechnique had thoroughly prepared the ground. It now swung into action. Filling in the missing details did not take long – only about six weeks.

The first round in establishing electromagnetism having been won by the French mathematicians, it was only fair that victory in the second round should fall to the British experimentalists. The genius who achieved this was the son of a blacksmith who began his career as an errand boy, apprenticed to a London bookseller. His name was Michael Faraday. Faraday, born in 1791, grew up in poor circumstances with little schooling and no mathematical training at all. However, he read the books that he was selling and binding, a pastime which provided him with sufficient education to write, at the age of twenty-two, a letter to Sir Humphry Davy, professor at the Royal Institution. It contained some notes on one of Davy's lectures, and the professor was sufficiently impressed to ask young Faraday to see him. The upshot of this interview was Faraday's appointment as assistant at the Royal Institution, a position worth twenty-five shillings a week and two rooms. Shortly afterwards Davy, having retired from his professorship, set out with his newly wedded wife on a grand tour of Europe. It says something for the

liberalism of the times that, although England was at war with Napoleon, special passports were granted and Davy was enthusiastically
received by his colleagues in Paris, and was even made a corresponding
member of the Institut de France.

There had been a last minute hitch in Davy's departure from England.
His servant refused to venture into France, and no substitute willing to
take the risk could be found. In despair Sir Humphry persuaded Faraday
to accompany him. While Faraday was hesitant because of the attendant
loss of status, the prospect of meeting the great scientists of Europe
tipped the balance in favour of the trip. It was the right decision, although at first Lady Davy proved a bit of a trial to him. The journey
immensely broadened Faraday's outlook, quite apart from acquainting
him personally with the leading scientific minds of France, Italy,
Switzerland and Germany. After two years the bookbinder's errand boy
returned to England as a man of the world, full of confidence in his
scientific future. He went back to the Royal Institution where in 1825
he was made director of the laboratory, and in 1833 Fullerian professor
of chemistry for life.

When in 1801 Count Rumford brought Davy to the Royal Institution, which he had founded and left in disgust, the scientific world was
astir with Volta's invention of the electric battery in the previous year.
A chemist by training, Davy was fascinated by the connection between
electricity and chemistry, and he made this the main subject of his research. Davy was a sound experimentalist, and saw that the basic requirement was a large and strong electric battery, which he immediately
constructed at the Royal Institution. Just as the French had profited by
laying down a sound mathematical basis which made progress easy for
Ampère, Biot and Savart, so the large battery of the Royal Institution
became a powerful tool for the British experimentalists.

Michael Faraday's first success in 1821 was to demonstrate, with great
experimental skill and use of the strong battery, an effect which had
already been implicit in Ampère's work but which the French had been
unable to discover. This was the spontaneous rotation of a magnet
around an electric current, and the rotation of a current about a magnet.
As Maxwell was to show later, this feature of rotation contains the
basic mathematical relation between electricity and magnetism.

There was another missing effect in the pattern of electromagnetism.
The French had shown that a current passing along a wire will produce
a magnetic field, but nobody had yet shown that a magnetic field would
produce a current. Now the problem was attacked by Faraday with the

impressive experimental armoury at his disposal. He made two large coils of wire, placing them close to each other. One of them he connected to his battery so that it created a strong magnetic field around the second coil. This second coil was joined up to a galvanometer (an instrument so named in honour of Galvani) which was able to detect an electric current. However, nothing happened, and even when the sensitivity of his equipment had been continuously improved, the expected effect failed to make its appearance. One wonders whether Faraday, who was a pious man, may have been dismayed at the apparent perversity of the Creator in fashioning electromagnetism in a lopsided manner. He could not, of course, know that the symmetry for which he had been looking in vain did in fact exist – but only at temperatures close to absolute zero. It was eventually discovered a century after his time.

Faraday had given up his efforts at finding the current in 1824. Disappointed by the negative result, he turned for a while to other researches, but his failure kept haunting him. Then, in 1831, he wrote:

> . . . Still it appeared very extraordinary, that as every electric current was accompanied by a corresponding intensity of magnetic action at right angles to the current, good conductors of electricity when placed within the sphere of this action, should not have any current induced through them, or some sensible effect produced equivalent in force to such a current.
>
> These considerations, with their consequence, the hope of obtaining electricity from ordinary magnetism, have stimulated me at various times to investigate experimentally the inductive effect of electric currents. I lately arrived at positive results; and not only had my hopes been fulfilled, but obtained a key which appeared to me to open out a full explanation.

These sentences form a part of the opening passages of Faraday's fundamental paper on his discovery of electromagnetic induction, read before the Royal Society at its meeting on 24 November. While the Creator appeared to have stubbornly retained the lopsidedness of electromagnetism, he at least had let Faraday into the secret which was to change thoroughly the aspect of our lives. The story goes that when Faraday was asked by one of the titled ladies at the Royal Institution whether the experiment that he demonstrated would have any practical use, he replied: 'Madam, what is the use of a newborn baby?' Eventually the baby was to grow into a powerful giant.

In his experiments of 1831 Faraday used the same arrangement as he had done seven years earlier: one coil through which the current from a battery was passed, and a neighbouring secondary coil, unconnected to

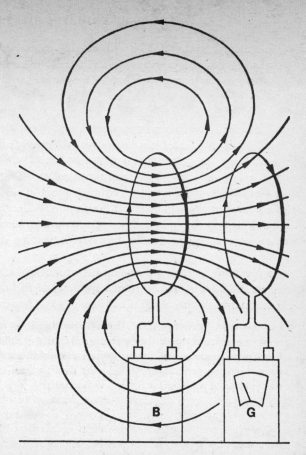

Fig. 19. For his discovery of electromagnetic induction Faraday used a 'primary' coil whose current, fed from a battery (B), generated a magnetic field which was picked up by a 'secondary' coil connected to a galvanometer (G). He only observed an effect when the current in the primary coil varied with time.

the primary one, to which a galvanometer was attached. The only difference was that the battery was stronger and the galvanometer more sensitive. Again, the result was negative. A steady current in the primary coil did not produce a steady current in the secondary one, but Faraday now noticed a curious phenomenon. A small transient current was observed in the secondary coil at the moment when the battery was connected to the primary. Equally, a transient current, but now in the opposite direction, appeared when the battery was disconnected from the primary. His conclusion was: '. . . the battery current through one wire, did, in reality, induce a similar current through the other wire, but that it continued for an instant only.'

Faraday's next step was to replace the magnetic field produced by the primary current with a bar magnet, which he pushed into the secondary coil. Again, a momentary current was observed, and another one in the opposite direction when the bar magnet was withdrawn. Electromagnetic induction had been discovered, but it was different from what Faraday had been expecting. He had indeed 'obtained electricity from ordinary magnetism', but a steady magnetic field still did not yield a steady current. Instead, the field had to be switched on and off, and then it produced an alternating current. As yet, Faraday's discovery did not provide an alternative source of electricity to that offered by the galvanic battery, and the newborn baby took quite some time in growing up.

The nine years following Faraday's fundamental discovery of electromagnetic induction were very busy ones for him. In a vast number of experiments he extended our knowledge in this field in a number of different directions. The most important results for the practical applications to come were, first, his discovery that induction between coils was greatly increased when they had been wound on a core of soft iron and, secondly, his observations on currents induced in wire loops rotated in a magnetic field. These features were to become the basis for the invention of the dynamo and the electric motor.

However, going beyond these experimental results, Faraday was striving all the time for a comprehensive interpretation of the phenomena that he had discovered. He revived Gilbert's idea of the 'lines of force', which he could trace in space with compass needles and iron filings. It was the correct way towards the goal, but he was unfortunately never able to reach it because of the limitations set by his lack of early education, which denied him the necessary theoretical insight and mathematical ability. Faraday's writings during this time reflect the hopes and frustrations which brought about his nervous breakdown in 1840 when he was approaching fifty. Although, after a rest of four years, he returned to work in his laboratory, he was never quite the same. After a short time he would always have to give up owing to giddiness and lapses of memory. Three years before his death, at almost seventy-six, the theory of electromagnetism was presented by Maxwell. Faraday could die content, although he must have been unable to comprehend the differential equations in which the results of his work were formulated. However, he did not live to see the newborn baby of

1831 grow into the powerful giant that changed the Western industrial pattern.

James Clerk Maxwell was born two months before Faraday made his great discovery. A descendant of the old Scottish family of Clerk of Penicuik, he was an athletic youth, fond of swimming, riding and walking, but he carried in him the seeds of the fatal illness which took away his mother when he was eight. As a youngster he sometimes spent his holidays at the house of William Thomson, later Lord Kelvin, at a time when the latter began to be interested in the mathematical theory of self-induction, discovered by Faraday, which was to play an important part in the development of the transatlantic telegraph cable. Here, possibly, was kindled Maxwell's interest in electromagnetism, for his first paper on the subject was published in 1855 under the title 'On Faraday's Lines of Force'. Maxwell thus took over where Faraday had had to leave off, and in the following years he developed Faraday's qualitative ideas into a rigorous theory on the mathematical basis provided by the French theoreticians of the École Polytechnique, particularly by Laplace and Poisson.

Maxwell spent most of his life in his native Scotland, and he was closely attached to his country house at Glenair. Nevertheless, his outstanding work was carried out during his four years (1860–64) as professor at King's College, London, when he was in close personal contact with the ageing Faraday. The end of his London period saw the publication of his famous paper, 'A Dynamical Theory of the Electromagnetic Field', which contains all the essential features of his great 'Treatise on Electricity and Magnetism' published in 1873, five years before his death at the age of forty-eight. The treatise presents the subject in such beautifully perfect form that nothing basically new has been added to it to this day.

The new field theory had an immense impact on the development of Western scientific thought, not only because it provides a clear understanding of electromagnetic action at a distance, but also because it reveals the nature of light as an electromagnetic vibration. It was one of those memorable instances in the development of natural philosophy when, suddenly, two large and so far unconnected chunks of our jigsaw puzzle of knowledge fit together. Experiments on the phenomena of light had been gathered, even from before the time of Huygens and Newton, and their results collated until they formed a well defined pattern of consistent observations. The building up of knowledge on electricity and magnetism has just been traced in this chapter. Now, at a stroke, all these fragments of experience had fallen into place as one grand design. In addition to this extremely satisfying result, the grand design was so all-embracing that it led to far-reaching predictions of phenomena still to be discovered. One of these predictions was the existence of as yet unknown electromagnetic waves, other than the vibrations noted by our eyes as light. It was clear that man had no sensory organs to record these, and that means of detecting them had still to be invented. Nor was it known whether such waves could be created. However, the powerful system of natural philosophy now allowed no doubt that these waves must exist. They were produced and recorded ten years after Maxwell's death by Heinrich Hertz, and they provided another important step in the story of white domination, to which we shall return in the next chapter.

As the title of Maxwell's first paper indicates, he was dealing with a new aspect of the phenomena of electromagnetism, its relation to mechanics, by investigating the forces which currents and magnets exert upon each other. Such forces had indeed been noticed as early as in the observations of Oersted and Ampère, but their proper place had to be found by the equations of Maxwell, who created a new branch of science called 'electrodynamics' which, from the blueprint given in the learned textbook, was soon to enter world affairs. The electromagnetic baby had now grown into the electrodynamic giant, and he was beginning to flex his muscles.

Gradually some applied use had been found for electricity, such as electroplating, and arc-lighting for streets and large halls. It was not all that much, but when Edison's feeble carbon filament light bulb graduated into the metal filament lamp, it was only a matter of time before electric lighting would displace the gas burner. The trouble was that its introduction required the development of a suitable source of electricity in sizeable quantity, and of a distribution network. Both required large capital outlay.

The galvanic battery has certain endearing features. In particular it provides energy without waste heat, which is the answer to any thermodynamic maiden's prayer. Unfortunately, like so many ethically edifying solutions, it has its drawback. The extraction of the necessary chemicals requires much greater energy than the waste heat in a coal-fired power station. So another source of electricity had to be found, and it had already been provided by Faraday. Turning a loop of wire in a magnetic field induces a current in the loop, a device that became known as the dynamo. Coupling up a large dynamo with a steam turbine we get

47, 48 The elusive forces of electromagnetism. *Right*, William Gilbert (1544–1603), physician to Queen Elizabeth; initiated basic research on magnetism. *Below*, two lodestones ground to a spherical shape (*terellae*): left, an armed *terella* with steel pole pieces; right, a *terella* engraved with lines corresponding to latitude and longitude.

49, 50 *Left*, drawing a spark from the nose. Electric experiments involving humans were a favourite pastime in the eighteenth century. *Below*, Emma Lyon (1765–1815), later Lady Hamilton, acted as receptionist and 'goddess of health' in an establishment effecting cures in electric beds.

51, 52 Experiments involving frogs' legs (*below left*), by Luigi Galvani (1737–1815), led to the erroneous theory that electricity was of animal origin. The first electric battery (*below right*), constructed by Alessandro Volta, revealed the true nature of Galvani's experiment.

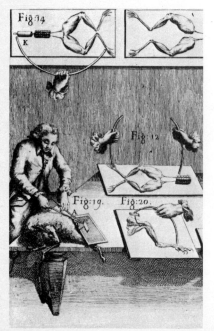

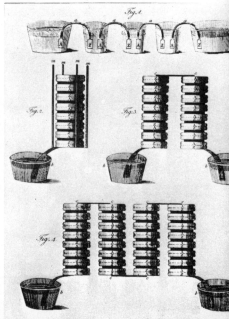

53, 54 *Above*, Humphry Davy (1778–1829) was initiator of electrical research at the Royal Society in London. *Right*, Michael Faraday (1791–1867), Davy's successor, discovered electromagnetic induction and the electrical nature of chemical forces.

55 James Clerk Maxwell (1831–1879) created the theoretical structure of electromagnetism, and predicted electromagnetic waves.

56 Mercury pumps yielding a high vacuum were first
developed for the commercial production of light bulbs.

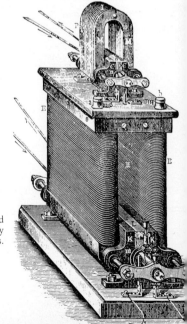

57 Wilde's dynamo. Wilde's claim to have invented
the dynamo caused serious contention with the Society
of Arts.

what is known as a turbo-generator, and these are the units that supply all the electricity we consume. Merely twisting a loop in a magnetic field seems a long way from constructing an efficient dynamo, but the principle is the same and the development can be left safely to the ingenuity of the electro-engineer.

The invention of the dynamo is shrouded in priority squabbles and litigation. It is generally accepted that it was invented by Werner Siemens, whose brother William took out an English patent in 1856 but then allowed it to lapse. In some rare cases textbooks mention the name of Henry Wilde, a man who in 1866 effected an improvement but could hardly claim the basic invention. This however, is what he did, and his claim led to a sequence of events which in the end involved me personally, seventy years after its beginning.

In 1900 the Society of Arts awarded Wilde its Albert Medal for the invention of the searchlight, to be presented to him by the Prince of Wales. Wilde replied with thanks that he was pleased to accept the medal for inventing the dynamo. 'The searchlight', said the Society gently. Wilde wrote back, not so gently, that his acceptance was for the dynamo. The rest of the correspondence shows an escalation in acrimony, with Wilde threatening legal action through his solicitors who wrote, somewhat pained: 'We exceedingly regret that we should have to write this letter, as we recognize the delicate nature of the situation, and that the writing of a lawyer's letter in response to an offer such as has been made to our client is probably without precedent.' The dispute worked itself to a crescendo, and then ended abruptly when the Society informed Wilde that the medal was being despatched forthwith by passenger train from Paddington – no Prince of Wales.

When in the early 1930s I came to Oxford, I found the laboratory very poorly equipped but discovered, in a corner, an ancient rusty contraption with two large coils on it which would have done well for a magnet. When I asked Lindemann, who was then professor of physics, for permission to take them he was aghast, informing me that this was Wilde's dynamo, which had been bequeathed to the department, together with the searchlight which indeed stood by its side. So I desisted, but was closely questioned some six years later as to the whereabouts of Wilde's dynamo. It had vanished and I was the natural suspect, until it transpired that it had by mistake been sold as scrap. However, it was not its unique historical value that had prompted the search for the dynamo, but the insistent desire of the Inland Revenue to levy death duties on it – twenty years after Wilde's demise. Perhaps the interest of the officials was sharpened by the fact that Wilde had thwarted them. He had made over most of his fortune to learned institutions in bequests as, for instance, the Halley lecture at Oxford.

Wilde, of course, had good reason for wanting to have the dynamo ascribed to him; it was a valuable invention involving big money. With the dynamo came the power stations, the distribution networks and, most important of all, the electric motor. By the end of the nineteenth century energy had definitely become the world currency, and the wealth of the white man now lay in his power production. Electricity does not actually produce power, and the delay in the growth of the giant had been due to the uncertainty as to where exactly electricity fitted into the pattern. Only gradually was it realized that, while electricity could not furnish power by itself, it provided the ideal means of transporting and managing it. The energy delivered through the rotation of the drive shaft of a heat engine has in some way to be utilized and distributed. It used to be handled, still in its mechanical form, through belts and gear wheels, all involving losses through friction, and was difficult as well as dangerous to operate. In any factory the steam engines had to be designed for their particular jobs because they, as well as the internal combustion engine, would only work efficiently within a narrow range of speeds.

It is much simpler to use a large turbo-generator which immediately converts the energy of its drive shaft into electric current. This electrical energy can then be split up into a wide network of cables and wires, through which it is fed safely and efficiently into a multitude of electromotors, each attached to a lathe, or a drill, or a vacuum cleaner, where it is transformed back into just the right amount of mechanical power required on the spot for a particular job. It can be switched on and off as wanted and, moreover, the output of mechanical energy can be varied by simple and efficient regulating devices in the electric circuits. Electricity provides an economy and flexibility in our energy household which was unknown before.

Another advantage of using electricity is its facility in transporting power over long distances. This is of particular importance when the primary source of power is located in a place far removed from industrial centres, as for instance a water reservoir in an inaccessible or uninhabitable region. Electric energy from the water-driven turbo-generators can then be fed to the urban industrial plant through cables and, again, the flexibility of electric power provides an economic way of doing this. It is clearly important that the power loss in the cables should be as small as possible, which means that the resistance of the cables should not be too large. Accordingly, they have to be made of a good electrical conductor, such as copper. Copper, however, is expensive, and the cost of the power line could easily defeat its purpose. Going back to our two little equations on page 152, we see that when we substitute volts in the second one from the first we get

$$watts = amperes^2 \times ohms$$

which shows that, for a given resistance in ohms of our power line, the dissipation in it, measured in watts, increases with the square of the current. This must therefore be kept as small as possible. Rewriting the original second equations as

$$amperes = watts/volts$$

we see that for a given power dissipation, measured in watts, we can decrease the current by simply increasing the voltage.

Fortunately Faraday had already discovered that electrical energy of low tension and high current can easily be changed into the same amount of power, but of high tension and low current, by choosing the number of turns in his two coils accordingly. Such a device is called a transformer, and it is simply attached to the generator at the power station, from where it is fed into the overhead grid of high tension cables at, say, 300,000 volts, only to be transformed back on arrival, hundreds of miles away, into our domestic appliances of 100 or 200 volts. Thus electricity has become the willing handmaiden of power production. She does not provide us with energy currency, but without her we would find it difficult to spend it.

The silent giant of electrodynamics has provided the white man with a sledge-hammer tool to assert his dominance over the globe. However, he also has a little sister called electronics who is less obtrusive and less powerful, but whose gentle grip on the globe has held the rest of mankind in even tighter bondage. We shall meet her later.

The beginning of the nineteenth century brought with it another and quite unexpected aspect of the electromagnetic forces, which turned natural philosophy in a very different direction but which was to become as important to our world as the whole of electrical industry. We said in the beginning of this book that the discovery of any new instrument or new technique is bound to disclose new vistas. It lies in the nature of experimental inquiry that we cannot foretell what are going to be the things that will be shown to us, but it is quite sure that our horizon will be widened in one way or another. The voltaic battery turned out to be one of the most powerful weapons in the armoury of the experimental philosophers, since it opened up many new vistas. It had led to the discovery of the laws of electricity, and prepared the way for its far-reaching practical uses. In addition it had revealed the true nature of light and, going along a quite different path, was to explain the cohesive forces of matter and the mechanism of chemistry.

Since the battery, unlike the Leyden jar, would deliver electricity in a steady and safe manner, it is not surprising that its study was taken up immediately by many scientists, and some of them were bound to strike it lucky. In May 1800, only a few weeks after Volta's announcement of his invention, Nicholson and Carlisle in London dipped the wires from their battery into a jar of water and saw little bubbles rise from the ends. It did not take them long to ascertain that they were oxygen and hydrogen gas, the constituent elements from which water is made up, and they concluded, rightly, that electricity was capable of chemical action. A few months later, Ritter in Germany deposited metallic copper electrically from a salt solution, and in 1807 Humphry Davy at the Royal Institution obtained two new elements, sodium and potassium, in the same way. These experiments, which were later continued with much success by Faraday, strongly suggested two things: first, that the basis of chemical reactions was electricity, and secondly, that the immensely strong forces which hold matter together were electromagnetic. Both these ideas proved to be correct.

When in the fourth century B C Democritus postulated that matter is not continuous but is made up of atoms, he also provided them, in his speculations, with little hooks and eyes holding them together. In later antiquity and in the Middle Ages people thought that the cohesive force was similar to that which makes a stone fall, i.e. gravity. However, the fact that the fragments of a broken object do not join up again when they are put together made this idea untenable, and Galileo, as we have seen, tried to get over this difficulty by postulating the existence of a vacuum in the interior of matter. Now, the observation that solid pieces of metal could be formed by means of an electric current made it almost certain that it also was an electric force which held the metal together. It took well over a century, and another great step in physical thinking, to prove that all things such as rock, metal, wood and, in fact, our own bodies, are bound into shape by electromagnetic forces. The road to the final proof, which was only obtained in the 1920s, was long and arduous, but since the days of Davy its outcome was never seriously doubted.

We have left chemistry with the account of the alchemists trying to make gold and inventing gunpowder instead. The same stage in the art of transforming matter from one form into another had been reached at the same time, or even earlier, by other great civilizations. The only difference which the white man's new experimental philosophy made to this state of affairs was the persistence of its practitioners in the face of disappointing results. Many new substances were created in their alembics, and while there was some limited use for a few of them, the sheer complexity of the results defied all attempts at systematization. Moreover, chemical research suffered from a certain lack of respectability, partly because some of its adepts, such as Paracelsus, used their products for medicinal purposes, often with dire consequences. It is known that Newton spent long years in chemical studies, but in the end destroyed all his records of them.

Nevertheless, it was in these early days of the Royal Society that the first substantial advance in chemistry was made by Robert Boyle, who published the *Sceptical Chymist*. It contains the basic idea of chemical elements which, through combination with each other in given proportions, formed the large variety of substances which we encounter. Continuing this work, Hooke discovered the important process of oxydation by observing that air 'preyed upon' charcoal. The next important step was taken by Lavoisier, who introduced quantitative methods by carefully weighing both the partners in a chemical reaction, and also their product. Finding the weight always unchanged, he enunciated the fundamental law of conservation of mass. There can be little doubt that this concept had a profound effect on the formulation of the other conservation law, that of energy, which followed eighty years later. The final synthesis of these ideas, and of those supplied by other great chemists like Black, Cavendish, Scheele and Priestley, was provided by a Manchester schoolteacher, John Dalton. Dalton's atomic theory, on which all modern chemistry is based, was published in 1808, one year after Davy's work had suggested the electric nature of chemical forces.

It cannot be our task to follow the breathtaking development of chemical research in the nineteenth and twentieth century, but we should mention the work of Fritz Haber who, in 1913, succeeded in the industrial fixation of nitrogen. Nitrogen in element form is abundant, forming 80 per cent of the earth's atmosphere, but is hardly available in compound form, except for deposits in Chile. On the other hand, nitrogen is essential for plant growth, and is the basic constituent of manure. It began to be realized at the end of the nineteenth century that the nitrates from Chile would soon be insufficient to furnish adequate supplies for intensive agriculture in the densely populated regions of the world, and the tapping of the unlimited supply of atmospheric nitrogen became one of the major achievements of German science. In addition to their use as fertilizers, nitrates are also the chief ingredient of explosives. Thus, when fixation was achieved on the industrial scale one year before the outbreak of World War I, it made Germany independent of Chilean nitrates for her fields and her guns. Twenty years later his country expressed its gratitude to Haber by expelling him as an 'undesirable Jew'.

Recognition and exploitation of the electromagnetic forces is one of the major achievements of the Western method of experimental philosophy. During the eighteenth century science had become a steadily growing force in the educational pattern of white civilization. The industrial revolution had drawn an ever increasing proportion of the population actively or passively into the orbit of scientific thinking. This process was accelerated throughout the nineteenth century till, at the end, there was no difficulty in training children into technicians competent to handle and service machinery based on forces hardly known a hundred years earlier. Being a technician, with a technician's way of thinking, had become an everyday occupation in the Western world. Out of Alessandro Volta's battery in 1800 had grown electrodynamics and chemical engineering, which were to enhance the white man's power over his neighbours still further.

CHAPTER SEVEN

Communication and computation

The white domination of the globe had began with the Portuguese success in combining a new and versatile type of seagoing ship, the caravel, with the use of scientifically developed navigational aids in the form of instruments and mathematical cartography. Here the only basically new device to be developed until the twentieth century was the marine chronometer, which owes its inception to the work of Robert Hooke, and which for the first time permitted accurate determination of longitude. This is not to say that existing navigational devices were not greatly improved, but nothing fundamentally new was added. Much the same can be said about the sailing ship. The decisive step, taken in the fifteenth century, had been the replacement of the single mast, that had served man for thousands of years, by a many-masted vessel which enabled use to be made of the varied wind patterns encountered on the global oceans. Here, too, nothing fundamentally new had been added to the original idea, although improvements had changed the craft out of all recognition. The caravel was succeeded by the galleon, the galleon by the frigate and so on, until the arrival of the five-masted clipper at the beginning of the twentieth century. That also was the end of the big sailing ships.

As early as 1708 Papin had suggested to the Royal Society the possibility of a boat driven by steam, but it was not until a whole century later that the first steamer was operated. In 1787 a young American portrait painter, Robert Fulton, went to England where he met, among others, James Watt. Fulton became imbued with the new spirit of the industrial revolution and of power production, and decided to give up painting in favour of engineering. He moved to Paris where, in 1803, he demonstrated a steamboat driven by paddle wheels on the Seine, a few miles above the city. His next success was a trip of 150 miles up the Hudson river, but for a time steamboats remained as novelties for joy-

rides before becoming important in river transport. Serious transatlantic crossings only took place after 1830, and for a long time the
steam engine merely acted as an auxiliary propulsion system to sailing
ships. The balance gradually shifted towards main use of steam engines,
particularly after the paddle-wheel was replaced by the propeller, and
the wooden hull by iron. One of the drawbacks of the steamship was the
need to provide a chain of coaling stations, but the opening of the Suez
Canal in 1869 brought great advantages to the steamer. Nevertheless, in
1870 84 per cent of the world tonnage still used sail only, and even in
1900 sailing ships still made up 40 per cent of the total.

This remarkable retention of sailing craft is simply a testimony to its
successful development as a means of strengthening the white grip on
the globe. Fast and efficient communication over the ocean routes had
been the backbone of Western domination, and the maritime nations
had throughout the centuries made a supreme effort in strengthening it.
In fact, the main reason for the relatively slow development of steam
navigation was due to the immense ingenuity that had been devoted to
improving sailing ships. In the end these had even become a shade too
successful, for if they had been less efficient they would have encouraged
faster improvement of power-driven vessels, which clearly were the
coming thing. As regards passenger transport, these ships too have had
to give way, in their turn, within a few decades to the jet aircraft.

It was the development of the ship as a means of fast and efficient
transport, rather than its use as a warship, that was the determining
factor in Western domination of the world. Guns were mounted on
ships at an early date, and they were sometimes used to bombard coastal
cities or to support a landing. However, as we have seen, they were
employed by the colonizing powers not merely so much for the conquest of territory as for blasting one another from the surface of the sea.

The advent of the railway, too, had the mainly indirect effect of
helping the Western countries to become more efficiently industrialized
rather than of opening up or administering new territories. The one
notable exception was India, where the creation of a well-administered
rail network proved a valuable aid in retaining foreign rule over a large
and densely populated country. In America the transcontinental railways
did not cause the decimation of the native population, but merely
hastened it. In an examination of the history of scientific concepts that
led to white domination, the railway is of little importance since it
involved no new ideas. With the development of the steam engine, it
became a foregone conclusion that, sooner or later, it would find its use

in transport. Rail tracks instead of roads had been employed in mines well before the steam locomotive rode on them. Equally, the motor-car with its versatile internal combustion engine gained importance in the first place as means of internal transport in industrialized countries, but came too late to play a significant part in colonial exploitation.

There exists, however, one field in which the internal combustion engine has led to a significant breakthrough, and that is in aviation. Prehistoric man already expressed his desire to fly like a bird, as shown in the legend of Daedalus and Icarus. The earliest attempts to do so, of which we know, go back to the Middle Ages. Leonardo da Vinci designed, but probably never built, a flying machine, and in 1680 Giovanni Borelli, a friend of Galileo's, proved in his book *De motu animalium* that the ratio of muscle power to weight in man was too small to achieve flight. Borelli turned out to be right, but this did not deter people from breaking their necks in attempts which, even today, are still going on.

Man's dream of sailing through the air was first fulfilled after he had realized that air itself has weight. In about 1670 Francesco de Lana, professor at Brescia, suggested the use of a boat to be suspended from four large copper balloons which had been evacuated. The idea was fundamentally correct except that, in order not to be crushed by the atmospheric pressure, the copper balloons would have had to be prohibitively heavy. The idea of being lifted from the earth by a contraption that is lighter than air was a direct consequence of the researches of the natural philosophers of the seventeenth century. It was scientifically sound, and led to its practical realization a century later when the expansion of air on heating had been investigated by the physicist Jacques Charles and was fully understood. It all happened with enormous rapidity within one year: 1783.

After preliminary experiments with paper bags filled with hot air, the brothers Joseph, Jacques and Étienne Montgolfier of Annonay, near Lyons, constructed a linen globe about 30 feet in diameter with an opening at the bottom, through which it could be filled with hot air from a fire. On 5 June 1783 they let the balloon rise at their home town. Watched by a large crowd, it immediately ascended to a great height, but came down after ten minutes when the air in it had cooled, two miles from the starting-point.

The Montgolfiers' spectacular success aroused much enthusiasm throughout France, and Jacques Charles in Paris decided to repeat it, but with the difference that hydrogen gas (which is lighter than air) was to be used instead of hot air. This was to obviate the rapid descent due to cooling which had occurred with the Montgolfier balloon. On 27 August an immense crowd gathered at the Champ de Mars to see the ascent, undeterred by a terrific shower of rain which drenched them a few minutes after the balloon had risen. Because the balloon was filled with hydrogen, the cooling rain had little effect on its performance. It rapidly gained height and then drifted away, coming down after three quarters of an hour near Gonesse, fifteen miles away, where it was promptly torn to shreds by the terrified villagers.

In the meantime, the Montgolfiers had prepared a larger and beautifully decorated balloon which, on 19 September, they demonstrated at Versailles before king, queen and the assembled court. It ascended to 1,500 feet and after eight minutes came down in the wood of Vaucresson, delivering safely the first three air passengers: a sheep, a duck and a cock, which was the only one to suffer discomfort when it had been kicked by the sheep in the excitement of take-off.

Human flight was to come still later in the same year. In October Pilâtre de Rozier, curator of the royal natural history collection, made several ascents in a captive hot air balloon, and on 21 November he and a companion travelled in it from the Bois de Boulogne for five miles across Paris. A few days later, on 1 December, Charles and his balloon builder Robert took off from the Tuileries in a hydrogen balloon which took them, in two hours, to the village of Nesle, twenty-seven miles away. This clearly established the superiority of the gas-filled balloon over the Montgolfier type, and Charles perfected it to the standard form still in use today. Efforts at steering and propelling balloons soon followed, culminating in the spectacular airship development by Count Zeppelin in Germany. Regular transatlantic crossings on a commerical basis began in 1936, but were discontinued when in the following year the hydrogen-filled ship burst into flames on landing. Although since then helium gas, a non-inflammable substitute for hydrogen, has become available in large quantity, further use of airships has never passed beyond the planning stage because of the superiority established by the airplane. In spite of its successful development, the lighter-than-air vehicle never became a viable form of inter-continental transport.

It was the airplane, and particularly its jet variety, that was to replace surface shipping on a world-wide scale. Unlike the airship, which was the result of scientific discovery and planning, the heavier-than-air transport owes its success to the enterprise of dedicated amateurs. After the hope of human-powered flight had been given up, the steam engine was tried as a propulsion mechanism but, again due to an unfavourable power to weight ratio, experimental craft of this kind never, in the truest sense of the word, got off the ground. Models which flapped their wings like birds had long been discarded, and efforts were concentrated on the 'soaring' of birds with their wings held still. It was by supplying such a glider with a light internal combustion engine driving propellers that the brothers Wilbur and Orville Wright scored their first success in 1903 at Kitty Hawk, North Carolina. Once it was realized that flight with heavier-than-air machines was feasible, their development was rapid. Ten years later the combat aircraft had found its use in war on a large scale.

The lift experienced by a bird's wing is a phenomenon whose scientific treatment requires a combination of complex experiments and advanced mathematics. Early work by Newton, Bernoulli, D'Alembert and Euler had led to fundamental laws of fluid friction, but it was not until after the practical demonstration by the Wright brothers that 'aerodynamics' became a field of serious study. Then experimentation with different shapes of the wing made fast progress, leading to the modern airliner of today. The propulsion by means of a screw based on the ship's propeller gave way, during World War II, to the use of the jet. Although the jet may appear a modern development to us, its basic principle of operation had been fully understood for centuries, and had been operated in the first century AD by Hero of Alexandria. It is also widely used as a lawn sprayer. The rocket, driving modern space vehicles, is an equally ancient invention, having been used in Chinese fireworks for a thousand years or more.

Both airplane and rocket vehicles owe their rapid development to their use in warfare, and it cannot be in doubt that they have played a significant part in white domination of the world. However, they are latecomers in this process and, as for instance in the last war, have been used by an Asiatic civilization against the Western powers. It should, however, be noticed that, while jet and rocket rely on long known scientific principles, their use has been made largely possible only by modern forms of telecommunication and electronic guidance that are based on the fundamental researches in electromagnetism in the nineteenth century.

After Stephen Gray's discovery of electrical conduction, the transmission of a signal along a wire was repeatedly suggested, and some practical attempts were made but without much success. The main difficulty was in the receiver, for which a spark or the motion of a pith ball were tried. After Oersted's observation in 1820, the deflection of a magnet needle by a current offered better prospects, and in 1833 Gauss and Weber at Goettingen communicated with each other in this way over a distance of one and a half miles. At about the same time, Joseph Henry at the Smithsonian Institution in Washington made similar experiments, and invented the electromagnetic receiver which was to revolutionize telegraphy.

However, for reasons of ethics he refused to take out a patent on it. The idea was taken up by an American design artist, Samuel Morse, who pursued it energetically and also invented the code made up of dots and dashes which bears his name. In 1838 Morse demonstrated his device before President van Buren and, with an appropriation by Congress, he constructed a telegraph line of forty miles between Washington and Baltimore. It worked perfectly, but the US Postmaster General decided that the telegraph was 'a toy' that would never pay its way, and further government support was withdrawn. Undaunted, Morse enlisted private capital, and by 1851 fifty companies in America operated telegraph lines. He was equally unsuccessful in gaining European patents, but eventually a number of states who used his system made *ex gratia* payments to him.

The introduction of the telegraph coincided with the development of the railways which, using electrical signalling between stations, provided an important field of application. Sending instantaneous messages over long distances began to furnish Western man with a most important adjunct in his hold over the non-white world. Until then, the fastest message to distant parts relied on the speed of ships, and it is clear that the use of the telegraph increased in significance the greater the distance that had to be covered. This gave much impetus to the laying of submarine cables, which were first used in 1851 between England and France. This first venture also demonstrated the hazards involved since, at the original attempt one year earlier, the cable broke shortly after having been put into operation. In spite of this warning a transatlantic cable was laid in 1857, but broke in the process. The next cable, between Ireland and Newfoundland, was laid in the following year only to be abandoned after it broke three months later. Then, however, the following year brought final and lasting success. Much of the perseverance in achieving long-distance cable telegraphy is due to William Thomson, later Lord Kelvin. His cable design, based on theoretical understanding of the factors involved, triumphed in the end over the originally adopted conventional ideas, and his invention of a sensitive recording device turned a financially hazardous undertaking into a success story.

Kelvin is the supreme example of the nineteenth-century scientist who turned his outstanding mathematical ability with equal success to the fundamental problems of physics and to their practical applications. His work ranged from the theory of heat over the phenomena of fluid flow and electromagnetism to speculations on the age of the earth, to all of which he made basic contributions. In the field of practical application of science, in addition to his work on various aspects of the transatlantic cable, he dealt with the development of a mariner's compass to be used on iron ships, a depth sounding device, a tidal gauge, and a tidal predictor. He wrote 660 scientific papers and took out 70 patents. Kelvin was the last *uomo universale* of science, a man who could turn his powerful and immensely versatile brain with advantage to any subject. He certainly was an extraordinary personality, but his comprehensive grasp was only made possible by the seemingly complete state of nineteenth-century exact science, which is now termed 'classical physics'. He lived long enough to see the crumbling of this proud edifice of knowledge at the turn of the century, and he was immediately aware of its significance. Kelvin was eighty when the very first stirring of that immense revolution in physics, to which we will turn later, appeared. His greatness is perhaps best shown by the remarkable open-mindedness with which this old man accepted that the kind of science he had taught and practised for sixty years was coming to an end.

Kelvin's life span roughly coincided with that of Queen Victoria, and he was very much a child of his age with its idea of a *Pax Britannica*, the beneficent extension of the white man's domination of the globe. It was an age of social and intellectual stability, characterized by a firm belief in the permanence of the human institutions created by Western man. Kelvin was knighted in 1866 in recognition of his work on the transatlantic telegraph, raised to the peerage in 1892, became president of the Royal Society in 1890, and received the Order of Merit in 1902. He was a mild-mannered, courteous man whose modesty and approachability endeared him to generations of students. Until the age of forty-five he lived in modest circumstances, but then became wealthy through his inventions. The first thing he did after coming into money was to spend it on his ocean-going yacht *Lalla Rookh*, to which he invited his friends and on which Queen Victoria herself once sailed. Being forever active, cruising did not prevent Kelvin from working when he was struck by an idea, which was often. One of his closest friends, the great Helmholtz, wrote:

Thomson presumed so far on the freedom of his surroundings that he always carried his mathematical notebook around with him. In the midst of the company he would begin to calculate, which was treated with a certain awe by the party. How would it be if I accustomed the Berliners to the same proceedings? But the greatest naïveté of all was when on the Friday he had invited all the party to the yacht and then, as soon as the ship was on her way, he vanished into the cabin to make calculations, while the company was left to entertain each other.

As early as 1853 Kelvin had considered the possibility of electromagnetic waves. Their existence had then been postulated in 1864 by Maxwell, and they were experimentally demonstrated by Heinrich Hertz in 1885. Attempts by Righi and Lodge at using the waves to transmit signals met with only limited success, and the stupendous development of wireless telegraphy is entirely due to a young Italian physicist, Guglielmo Marconi. Not finding much encouragement in his own country, Marconi went in 1896 to England where the Post Office and the Admiralty supported his efforts. After establishing radio communication across the Channel and then between ships on the high seas, Marconi scored his greatest triumph when, on 12 December 1901, his signals sent from Poldhu in Cornwall were received in St John's, Newfoundland.

There is a certain resemblance between Marconi's success and the discovery of America. Columbus had endeavoured to sail to China, basing his plan on a faulty estimate of the earth's circumference, and would have perished if America had not been in the way. It had been assumed, on the existing knowledge of their behaviour, that electromagnetic waves could only be received at a short distance before, like light rays, they would be lost in space due to the curvature of the earth. Marconi, in complete disregard of the theoretical predictions, or perhaps in ignorance of them, pursued his experiments, not realizing that their success was due to the unknown fact that, at a height of about 100 miles above its surface, the earth is surrounded by an electrically conducting layer, the ionosphere. The radio waves which would have passed from the transmitting aerial out into space are, in fact, reflected back to earth by the ionosphere, and thus travel around the globe, held captive by this electric envelope. Like America, the ionosphere was not predicted and, but for its unexpected presence, Marconi's name would have vanished from the annals of science as would have Columbus's ships without the obstacle of America. This might appear a disappointing story but for one fact: it illustrates the strength of natural philosophy, which lies in its experimental approach. Now and then an experiment

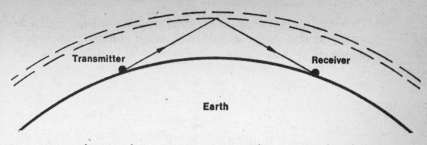

Fig. 20. *Marconi's spectacular success in transmitting radio waves over long distances was due to their reflexion by a conducting envelope (the ionosphere) surrounding the earth at a height of about 100 miles. When carrying out these experiments he was, however, ignorant of the existence of the ionosphere.*

carried out in the face of unfavourable 'established' views can lead to a surprising breakthrough.

There can be no doubt of the immense role played by radio communication with its multifarious aspects in the progress of Western science and technology. From sending messages to the direction finding and location of distant objects by radar, the use of electromagnetic waves has immensely increased the scope of earlier operations and added a host of entirely new ones. From the first, radio and television, through their immediate contact with the great mass of the people, completely revolutionized the channels of information and gained vast political importance. They have also, of course, played their part in the white man's impact on the rest of the world.

However, most of these developments would have been impossible to achieve but for the creation of a new technology, called 'electronics'. When the laws governing the flow of electricity were elucidated, in the early nineteenth century, it was never clear what was the nature of this electrically charged fluid that passed through the wires. The inability to define electricity scientifically, at a time when it was already being sold as power, brought with it the need for legal definition, resulting in the new type of offence of 'stealing electricity'. Faraday's discovery that in electrolysis a definite quantity of electric current always resulted in the same amount of copper atoms being deposited, strongly suggested that electric charge was composed of atomistic units. In other words, it appeared that electricity, like matter, was particulate, but it had to remain an item of speculation whether the elementary carrier of electricity had material existence. In 1897 J. J. Thomson in Cambridge, studying the flow of electricity through highly rarefied gases, discovered this elementary carrier of charge, which was to be named the electron. It has unit negative charge and turned out to be a particle of very small mass, almost 2,000 times lighter than the lightest known atom, that of hydrogen.

The implications of this discovery for the fundamental aspects of physics were tremendous, and we shall have to deal with them later. Here we are concerned with the technical applications of this new knowledge. The first thing to realize was that the original naming of electric polarity unfortunately happened to be the wrong one. The current does not run from the positive pole, which was suspected to hold a surplus of electric charge, to the negative one, but vice versa. However, this does not alter the current laws themselves since the electrons always stay in the metal. Thomson had been able to identify them because, in his experiment, the electrons had been freed from the metal into the vacuum of the discharge tube, and it was this liberated state which permitted their use in the technology of electronics.

By means of electrically charged plates inserted into the vacuum tube, the electrons in it could be made to follow commands given by changes in the charge. Owing to their small mass and negligible inertia they would follow the command from the plates instantaneously, however rapidly the charge in the plates was changed. The most important step in the development of electronics was to arrange the plates in such a manner that a stream of electrons passing through the tube could be altered in exactly the rhythm in which minute changes of charge took place in one of the plates. In other words, an electrically 'whispered' command in the steering plate could be faithfully amplified to an exactly corresponding 'roar' in the current. It is this amplifying action which made the electron tube the most versatile device in the thousands of different electrical circuits used in electronics.

It cannot be our task to describe, even in rough outline, the manifold applications of electronic technology. Soon the vacuum tube found another application in generating electromagnetic waves of very much shorter wavelength than those that could be produced by the conventional means used so far. It was this type of short wave that made systems like radar possible, and these waves were also capable of piercing the ionosphere, which kept the longer waves confined to the envelope around the earth. Sent out into space, the short waves could be used to guide the rocket vehicles dispatched to the moon and to planetary space. Signals can be passed on to communication satellites orbiting the earth,

58, 59 Steam-powered paddle-wheels installed in tugboats (*above*) came into use during the mid-eighteenth century, before the advent of real steamboats. *Below*, in early boats the engine was employed merely as auxiliary propulsion to the use of sail.

60 *Below*, The Suez Canal (opened in 1869) brought about the ascendancy of the steamer over the sailing vessel.

61 Richard Trevithick's railroad at Euston Square, London, 1809. This, the first steam railway, started as a fairground attraction.

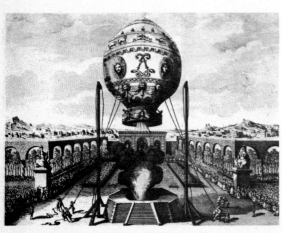

62, 63 *Above*, the Montgolfier hot-air balloon makes its first flight with human passengers (1783). A few days later, the physicist Jacques Charles (1746–1823) ascended in a balloon filled with hydrogen gas (*right*).

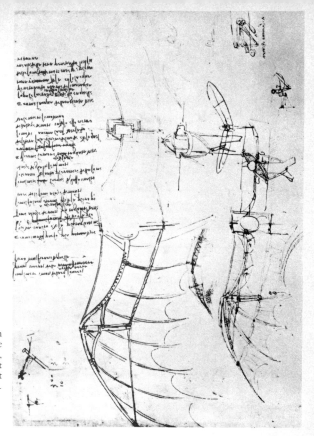

54, 65 Leonardo da Vinci's sketch (*right*) of a flying machine involved flapping wings. *Below*, the moment of take-off: the first aeroplane flight by the Wright brothers, 1903.

66, 67 *Above*, the *Great Eastern* laying the transatlantic telegraph cable in 1866. *Left*, William Thomson (1824–1907) later Lord Kelvin, who was closely associated with the cable operation, was equally successful in pure and applied science.

68, 69 *Below left*, a medal commemorating the rescue of 170 souls on 24 January 1909, when help was summoned by wireless telegraphy. *Below*, Dame Nellie Melba performing on the first advertised radio programme, June 1920, from the Marconi works in Chelmsford.

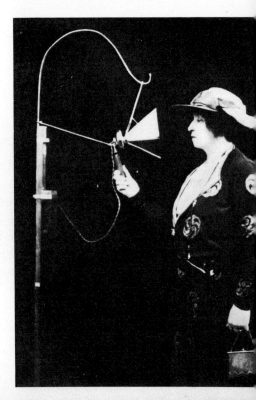

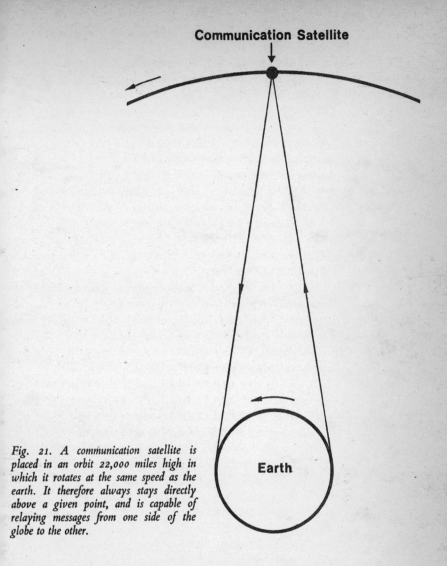

Communication Satellite

Earth

Fig. 21. A communication satellite is placed in an orbit 22,000 miles high in which it rotates at the same speed as the earth. It therefore always stays directly above a given point, and is capable of relaying messages from one side of the globe to the other.

and then relayed by them to distant parts of the globe. Receivers tuned to such short waves revealed that space is filled with signals originating from distant stars, and led to the new science of radio-astronomy. New vistas which at present have hardly been explored are opening before our eyes through this new and powerful tool of science.

For the better part of half a century the vacuum tube remained the essential tool of electronic engineering. Then, around 1950, its use began to be replaced and augmented for many purposes by a new device, the transistor. This consists of a crystal of semiconductive material. It had been known for a long time that certain chemical elements exist, such as germanium, which present the aspect of a half-way house between a metal and an insulator. Whereas metals like copper are crammed full of electrons available for electric conduction, and no such electrons are available in insulators, semiconductors possess just a few of these electrons. In a way they therefore behave like a vacuum tube in which the liberated electrons are few and far between. Being so diluted, the electrons in the crystal do not interfere with each other, and can receive and carry out commands like those in a vacuum tube. Among the many advantages of the transistor are its small size, its simplicity, and the fact that, unlike the vacuum tube, it does not generate heat. More and more of our standard electronic devices, such as radio and television sets, make use of transistors instead of vacuum tubes.

So far in this chapter we have talked about the various means of communication that have aided the West in dominating the world, and we have now been led into a discussion of their most versatile form, electronics. However, there exists another application of electronics which, while not primarily connected with communication, is transforming our life even more profoundly. It is the computer.

At the very outset of this book we defined natural philosophy as the experimental observation of events and regularities which are expressed in mathematical form. These mathematical expressions in which we cast the laws of nature are then used for predicting other events, and it is this power of prediction that provides the method with the economy of effort which has enabled the white race to achieve domination of the world. Ease and speed of mathematical calculation are the fundamental requirements for the operation of this philosophy. Methods to achieve this began at the end of the sixteenth century, with the invention and use of logarithms and the slide rule. Less than a century later Leibniz invented a mechanical calculating machine, and at the end of the nineteenth century electric operation of punched card indexes was used to make rapid and complex statistical calculations. These partly mechanical devices were far outdistanced by the electronic developments of the mid-twentieth century. The great advantage of the electronic computer over the earlier machines lies in the essentially unlimited, faithful amplification already mentioned, and the high speed of its performance.

There are two main types of electronic calculating machine, the analog and the digital computer. The difference between them corresponds to our basic forms of measuring and recording instruments. The analog computer deals with smoothly varying phenomena, as for instance the needle on the speedometer of a car indicates *continuously* the velocity of the vehicle. The hand of a clock, however, *counts* discrete intervals of time, each being one swing of the anchor escapement, and then adds up the number of intervals on the clock face. Leibniz's calculating machine or a cash register handles information of this second kind, whereas Kelvin's tide predictor relied on the observation and computation of smoothly varying functions.

Natural phenomena, of course, always fall into this last class, but the analog computers needed to handle them are not nearly as easy to design as digital computers, which are merely glorified adding machines. Nevertheless, the example of the clock shows us that even a smoothly varying quantity, like time, can be adequately measured with a discontinuously working counting device. In fact, when reading an electric instrument, or a wind meter, or a pressure gauge, we record numbers printed on the scale, unconsciously dividing a smooth function into finite steps. It is therefore clear that the much simpler and basically cheaper digital computer can perform very adequately most operations involving smoothly varying quantities. Mathematically speaking, the digital computer corresponds to the functions performed by simple arithmetic, whereas the analog computer deals with the problems of calculus. As is well known, these problems can often be solved arithmetically, never with complete accuracy but frequently with very good approximation.

Earlier we referred to the complex mathematics involved in aerodynamics, and it is here that the electronic analog computer has found a most useful field of application. The conventional mathematical approach is, owing to its complexity, very tedious and time-consuming, and was generally replaced by wind tunnel experiments which, however, are costly. The computer, on the other hand, can handle simultaneous changes of the many factors involved in air flow, and provide a fast and less expensive solution. Equally, an analog computer can be used to simulate a wide variety of rapidly changing conditions such as are encountered by the aircraft in flight. Such a flight simulator can feed into a set of cockpit instruments exactly the readings which a pilot will see when taking off, flying, or landing an airliner under all kinds of conditions, and therefore provides a safe and inexpensive training device for air crews.

A digital computer is basically extremely simple, consisting in essence of an enormous number of switches which can actuate each other. Like any simple switch, the computer element can be either 'on' or 'off', allowing no more than two numbers: o for the switch open and 1 for the closed switch. For the purpose of calculation this means that we have to write our ten numerals of the decimal system, o to 9, in a so-called binary code, consisting of only o and 1. For instance, for our 2 this code is 10, for 6 it is 110, and for 9 it is 1001. For 100 we must write 1100100, which means that, for this number, instead of our three digits we have to use no less than seven. This may appear a clumsy way of counting, but it is amply compensated for by the speed of operation which, in a modern computer, is about one hundred millionth of a second for each count.

In addition to the switching elements performing the arithmetic, the computer requires a memory in which interim results of the calculation can be stored until they are again required. The computer must also be given the correct orders for carrying out the desired calculation; it has to be programmed. This program, as well as the numbers to be used, have to be fed into the machine since, whatever people may believe, it cannot 'think' in our sense of the word. A computer can in fact make decisions; for instance, it can compare two results of its calculation and then select the larger or the smaller. However, the order to make this decision has to be written into its program in the first place. An early example of this was the use of computers in oil refineries. From the crude oil entering the plant a great number of petroleum products are derived, and the rate at which each is tapped off will affect the production rate of all the others in a rather complex manner. It is a time-consuming and not very straightforward mathematical exercise. The computer can now be programmed to solve with great speed all the equations involved and, in addition, decide what setting of the refinery stages will provide the most economic yield for any desired combination of products.

Thus, while the computer is not capable of original thought, it can help us think in an extremely effective manner by saving time and avoiding errors. Moreover, computer development and exploration of its use are still in the early stages. Since mathematical correlation is the backbone of our natural philosophy, it would be difficult to over-estimate the prospects which the computer holds in the future operations of science.

CHAPTER EIGHT

Landfall in a new world

'Italian navigator has reached the new world.' This was the text of the eagerly awaited code message sent from Chicago to Washington on 2 December 1942, informing Vannevar Bush, the chairman of the US National Research Defense Committee, of the first liberation of atomic energy by man. The experiment was being carried out by Enrico Fermi in an inconspicuous makeshift laboratory under the grandstand of the Chicago stadium. Bush's acknowledgment came in the form of a question: 'Are the natives friendly?' Fortunately they were; the reactor, stacked with uranium and graphite, was delivering energy at a steady rate without catastrophic results. This initial step into the new world of atomic energy heralded an age in the history of mankind in which domination of man over man was soon to take on another dimension, which within two decades was to defeat its original aim of annihilating the enemy. That fateful day in 1492 when the New World was reached marked the end of a voyage of discovery that had taken half a century to complete. The fifty years, starting in the 1890s, which led to the second 'new world', represent a profound revolution in Western scientific thinking of which the liberation of atomic energy was merely a by-product. While this by-product is having an immense, and probably decisive, effect on human affairs, it must be remembered that, but for the purposeful pursuit of natural philosophy, it would not exist. The road from the research establishment at Sagres to the Chicago grandstand is a straight one from which the white race never deviated. Its attraction has been the economy of effort which ensured its success.

Science in the nineteenth century had been a process of consolidation. Its development was consistent in exploring and exploiting earlier observation, which led to gratifying rewards in both fundamental knowledge and industrial technology. There still remained a number of unsolved problems, but it was confidently expected that these, too, would be explained within the framework of what we now call 'classical' physics. Seen in retrospect, it must be admitted that intellectual complacency in that period went a good deal further than was justified by the existing danger signs. These were visible in different, and seemingly unconnected, fields of science. Since Maxwell, light and other electromagnetic waves had been explained as vibrations – but vibrations of exactly what? An all-pervading substance, the 'ether', had been postulated as the carrier but, like the all-pervading fluids to explain heat and electricity postulated in earlier physics, the properties of this hypothetical ether became more and more difficult to accommodate within the rest of observations. Finally, in 1887, Michelson and Morley performed an experiment which dealt a death blow to the ether – with nothing to take its place.

Another warning was provided by the bright colours seen when mineral salts are added to a flame. They had been used by the chemists since the 1860s to identify elements. When the alchemists observed that light falling through a prism is fringed by the colours of the rainbow, they called it a 'spectrum', a ghost. With a suitably designed instrument, the spectroscope, light from any source can be split up into a number of lines of different colour, corresponding to the wavelength of light. Each element shows characteristic lines, which are used for identification, but the origin of these spectral lines remained a mystery. Since they differ from element to element, it was taken for granted that they must issue from the individual atoms in some as yet unexplained process.

When in 1897 J. J. Thomson discovered the electron, the fact that it was so much lighter than the lightest atom immediately suggested that electrons might be component parts of atoms. This, of course, ran counter to the accepted idea that the chemical atoms should be, as their name demands, *atomos*, i.e. indivisible. J. J. Thomson and Lord Kelvin in fact suggested atomic models, but its true structure was discovered in 1911 by Ernest Rutherford, who showed that atoms consist of a very small and extremely dense nucleus which is positively charged and is surrounded by a cloud of electrons. Contrary to expectation, Rutherford's experiments showed that atoms have a very open structure, consisting mostly of empty space with practically all the mass concentrated at the centre, and with the very much lighter electrons cruising about it in space. The similarity with the solar system appeared so striking that for some time scientists accepted the analogy as a correct interpretation of atomic structure. An elaboration of this model by the Danish physicist Niels Bohr, in 1913, further strengthened this idea since, for the first time, it provided a quantitative explanation for the enigmatic spectral lines. It all fitted in well with a miniature solar system – but, as we shall see, for a difference.

In the twenty years between Thomson and Bohr more things had changed than the concept of the atom. First of all, when Rutherford had postulated his model of the atom, he had used nuclear bullets for probing matter. The bullets had been discovered by a good-looking Polish research student, Marja Sklodowska, who had just married the French physicist Pierre Curie. Pierre had advised her to follow up, for her thesis, some odd observations made by Henri Becquerel at the École Polytechnique in 1896. One year earlier Conrad Wilhelm Röntgen in Germany had discovered a very penetrating radiation which he called X-rays, and since for the time being their origin remained obscure, looking for new radiations became the fashion. It was a free for all, and quite a number of radiations were 'discovered', most of which later proved spurious. Becquerel had an idea that minerals, after being exposed to sunlight, might emit penetrating rays, and he was successful with salts of uranium. However, he then found, almost by accident, that these salts gave out rays even if they had not been in sunshine, and at this point young Madame Curie enters the story.

She began work for her doctorate thesis by repeating and extending Becquerel's observation. To her surprise she discovered that a uranium-bearing mineral, pitchblende, radiated more strongly than even pure uranium, and the Curies concluded that it must contain some as yet unknown substance. In two years of extremely hard work under exacting conditions she extracted from five tons of pitchblende no more than one grain of two new elements, which she named radium and polonium, the latter in honour of her native country. The strange property of emitting radiation she called 'radioactivity'. After Pierre's death in 1906 Marie Curie continued her researches into radioactivity, but its ultimate explanation fell to Rutherford and his school. They discovered that the atomic nuclei in radium and polonium disintegrate spontaneously, ejecting the very energetic particles which were used in probing and elucidating the structure of the atom.

Quite unconnected with this work, Max Planck in Berlin tried theoretically to find a formula which would express in a very general form electromagnetic radiation in terms of energy, temperature and wavelength. When at last, in 1900, he found the solution, it turned out to his consternation that energy, like matter and electricity, is particulate in nature. This means that the light of the sun, for instance, does not

come to us as a smooth homogeneous stream but that it has grain structure. The fact that we do not perceive this is due to the smallness of the
grain. Its size is determined by a number that appears in Planck's formula,
and which is of atomic dimension. He called the energy parcels 'quanta',
and the number in his equation the 'quantum constant'.

Planck had no doubt of the correctness of his result or its profound
significance for physics and chemistry, but he did not like it. He was the
descendant of a long line of Prussian law-givers and was conservative in
outlook, being steeped in classical physics. He had tried in vain to get
rid of the constant in his formula, and when this proved impossible he
did nothing to advance or apply his theory. This was done five years
later by an unknown young man employed by the Berne Patent Office,
Albert Einstein. Unlike Planck, Einstein did not mind revolutionary
ideas when he applied, most successfully, the quantum theory to the
liberation of the electrons from a metal by light rays. In fact, he went so
far as to call the energy parcels 'arrows of light', thereby ascribing to the
quanta physical reality. But although Einstein's work provided a brilliant proof of the correctness of Planck's theory, Planck ignored it.

This does not mean that Planck was unaware of young Einstein's
work. When in the same year Einstein published his theory of relativity,
he hailed it as the most outstanding advance in theoretical physics.
Relativity did away, in the most elegant manner, with the difficulties of
the ether and of the Michelson-Morley experiment. Where the practitioners of established physics found no way out of the dilemma, the
lonely young man at the Patent Office started from the beginning, un-
trammelled by the shibboleth of accepted opinion. He built up a mathematical framework that was not unlike Newtonian mechanics, except
that he added to the three dimensions of space a fourth one, time, as an
equal partner. The speed of light acquires special significance in relativity, since it is taken as an upper limit for the velocity with which
knowledge of an event can be passed on. Simultaneity in the 'classical'
sense ceases to exist since there is no sense in talking about an event
before information of it can reach us. Light takes eight minutes in its
travel from sun to earth, but when we see an eruption on the sun it
would be incorrect to say that it took place eight minutes ago since, for
an observer on earth, it occurs when he sees it. There exists no physical
agency by which he could have obtained prior knowledge.

According to classical physics, a bullet could be speeded up to any
velocity if sufficient propellant charge were packed into the gun barrel.
It could even be made to travel faster than light – but this is not per-

mitted in relativity. The only way to prevent the bullet from reaching or exceeding this velocity is to make it progressively heavier as it is accelerated, until at light velocity its mass would be infinite. Experiments with fast nuclear particles show that this growth in mass does indeed occur, exactly as predicted by Einstein. This, in turn, means that mass and energy must be convertible into each other, and the relativistic formula for this transformation is very simple indeed. It says:

$$mass = energy/light\ velocity^2$$

and the only reason why we have failed to notice the attendant mass change when coal is burned, or in any other chemical reaction, is that the square of the light velocity is a very large number. It is a figure with 23 noughts, and dividing any conventional energy charge by it will give an immeasurably small result. However, the very much larger energies involved in nuclear reactions lead to quite noticeable 'mass defects'. Again Einstein's theoretical formula was proved correct.

It is, of course, tempting to compare Einstein's burst of genius in isolation with that of Newton, and there certainly are striking similarities. However, unlike Newton, Einstein was a poor scholar at school and did not distinguish himself at the university. While Newton's isolation was due to the plague, Einstein's seclusion was brought about by the fact that he was regarded as unfit to hold a permanent school-teacher's job. The position at the Patent Office, which he owed to the influence of his schoolfriend's father, provided the welcome and financially secure retreat that gave him time and peace to follow his lone studies. He later said that he never met a theoretical physicist until he was thirty years old. Einstein was twenty-six when he published most of his outstanding work, and we should remember that Newton's great achievements also go back to a short period of isolation in his youth. Einstein's case again shows that the original natural philosopher tends to be young.

The sheer variety in the multitude of new scientific discoveries recounted in the last few pages will probably leave the reader bewildered. However, this bewilderment is nothing compared with the confusion into which the world of physics had been thrown at the beginning of this century. We have, in fact, taken some trouble in concentrating on the relevant events, whereas at the time nobody could say which were the important results in a veritable morass of published data. One thing was already certain: the proud edifice of classical physics was cracking everywhere, threatening to crash down on its practitioners. There was one thought of salvation: classical physics had been so very successful that it could not possibly be completely wrong. In retrospect it is apparent that, rather than being wrong, classical physics was severely limited. The limitations, too, can now be seen to have manifested themselves fairly clearly by, say, 1910. Classical physics was the physics of human dimensions, and it failed when scientists tried to scale it down to the size of the atom or to scale it up to speeds never encountered in daily experience. This was a lesson which was hard to grasp and even harder to learn.

In many respects the Rutherford-Bohr atomic model was still quite classical. The electrons, like the planets, circle around the nucleus at distances which are large compared with its own size. It was tacitly assumed that electrons and nucleus had the properties of large-scale structures, like billiard balls, only very much smaller. It was, of course, somewhat worrying that the solid objects of our everyday world, like stone and iron, should mainly consist of empty space, populated only by a number of tiny whirling particles. Even so, these concepts were quite compatible with classical laws, but there were other aspects in the Bohr atom which presented a radical departure from large-scale physics. The electrons circling the nucleus do not emit electromagnetic radiation as classical physics requires for a rotating electric charge.

In addition, they cannot circle around the nucleus at *any* distance as a planet can, but only certain orbits are permitted which are determined by Planck's quantum constant. Radiation given out or received by an atom corresponds in the Bohr model to the 'jump' of an electron from one to another of the quantum orbits. These were all rules for which no reason could be found, and which for the time being had to be accepted because they proved most useful. The success of the model was, indeed, immense. The energy of the quantum jumps was found to yield exactly the wavelengths of the mysterious spectral lines. Moreover, the arrangement of the outermost electron orbits explains the differences in chemical behaviour of the atoms. The electric nature of chemical forces, first suspected by Davy and Faraday, was finding its explanation in the electron structure of the atom. However, in spite of these great successes, the voyage into the new world had only begun.

For a while Bohr tried to treat his atomic model as a special case of classical mechanics by introducing his 'correspondence principle' whereby, for each aspect of the quantized atom, a classical analogy was cited. This proved not very helpful, and physicists felt that they were engaged in a game with rules which had to be discovered while they were playing

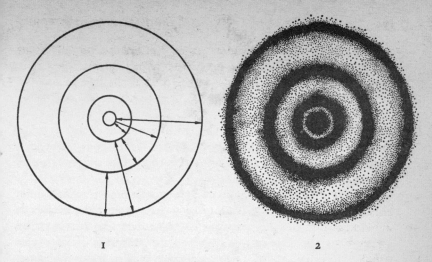

I   2

Fig. 22. The Rutherford-Bohr model of the atom was a miniature solar system in which the electrons circled the nucleus in well-defined 'quantized' orbits. Energy can be radiated or absorbed by transitions between orbits (1). Modern quantum mechanics has replaced the precise orbits by diffuse rings (2), indicating the probability of electron positions. Indeterminacy sets a fundamental limit to the accuracy with which the electron can be located.

it. Gradually it became clear that, as far as the atomic world was concerned, corrections to classical physics would lead nowhere and a radical departure was required.

There exists an interesting parallel here between political and scientific thinking. The beginning of the revolution in physics at the turn of the century was a relatively orderly process. It coincided with the growth of social democracy before World War I in which the innovators were striving for a gradual change in economic and political conditions without contemplating a violent overthrow of the established order. After the war, England and America tried to regain the old kind of life, shutting out all thought of the revolutionary influence of Russia. It was different in Europe, where civil disorder and inflation had completely undermined society, and a new generation grew up that had little use for the social values of the pre-war years. These young people, who saw no reason to respect the ethical precepts of their parents, were equally ready to make short shrift of the tenets of classical physics. It is therefore not surprising that most of the revolutionary advances in modern physics came from the somewhat cynical and uncompromising young generation in Europe.

The decisive step was taken by a brilliant young physicist in his early twenties, Wolfgang Pauli. He expressed, in mathematical form, a correction required for the Bohr atomic model, but pointed out that it was 'classically nondescribable'. Mathematical description of physical laws had, of course, been the aim of natural philosophy from the very beginning. However, even such equations as those for the flow of heat or electricity could always be visualized by everyday experience as a current of water. They all refer to large-scale phenomena, involving an enormous number of particles. Pauli, on the other hand, pointed out that we have no reason to suppose that events on the atomic scale can ever be compared with occurrences of our experience; they have to be considered in their own context, and not as anything corresponding to the classical laws which are based on large-scale observation. We can, as he did, give them names, but we should not accept these names as classical analogies of the happenings on the atomic scale. Pauli's step in relying on nothing but the mathematical formulation in our description of the atomic world constituted a profound departure from the traditional pattern of natural philosophy. Far from destroying its methods, it strengthened them by looking at classical physics as merely a special case that had grown out of human experience.

It was an impressive success for natural philosophy to realize that its mathematical interpretations still hold good in a world which is completely divorced from our everyday observation, and which we must forever fail to visualize. For instance, in classical physics a wave and a particle are completely different things; a wave is a ripple seen on a pond, and a particle is a billiard ball or a bullet shot from a gun. On the atomic scale this difference largely disappears because the mathematical description for these things becomes rather similar. Already in 1905, when Einstein described the quanta of radiation as arrows of light, he had thereby given them particle aspects, although dozens of well-known classical experiments had shown that light has wave character. Twenty years later a young law student who had turned scientist, Prince Louis de Broglie, turned Einstein's argument around. Particles, he said, might behave like waves. At first it seemed a lunatic idea, but when shortly afterwards American and British physicists sent electrons through an apparatus to detect waves, they indeed found a wave pattern emerging from this stream of particles. Science clearly was in confusion, and Sir William Bragg voiced the general opinion when he said: 'We teach the particle theory of matter on Mondays, Wednesdays and Fridays and the wave theory on Tuesdays, Thursdays and Saturdays.'

Soon the Bohr atom lost all similarity with the solar system, and its precise planetary orbits were replaced by the diffuse rings of a wave pattern. Erwin Schrödinger, only one year after de Broglie, applied the wave concept to the atom – and it immediately worked. Having shed its classical interpretation, the Bohr model, in its new 'quantum mechanical' form, proved not only manageable but able to provide all the correct answers. Max Born, one of the pioneers of the new science, said: 'As usual, mathematics has been wiser than visual imagination.' But one awkward question remained: where in this diffuse ring was the electron?

The answer was provided only one year later by Werner Heisenberg. It was simple but, at first sight, disappointing; it said: we don't know and we never will be able to know. Again it was a young man of barely twenty-six who provided this surprising solution, which was to become the central axiom of quantum mechanics. It was a triumph of clear thinking, free from all traditional encumbrance and from concepts that had been retained because they appeared self-evident. Nothing, said Heisenberg, is evident except direct observation, and it is only observation which is allowed to enter theory. Such caution was indeed necessary, because the consistent picture that had been provided by classical physics had often encouraged scientists to use it as a foundation, and not to go back at each step to re-examine the secure nature of these seemingly basic tenets. Now, as Pauli had warned and Heisenberg reiterated, the position was different. Science was moving into an unexplored area where, nevertheless, observation had often led to the construction of models on the customary classical basis as, for instance, in equating the atom with a planetary system.

Heisenberg started his theoretical considerations with the most basic experiment, the location of a particle and the determination of its speed. It cannot be located, he argued, without using a probe of some kind but, when applied, this probe was itself bound to alter the position and velocity of the particle under investigation. Since the particle was on the atomic scale, and not a billiard ball or a bullet, the degree of this interference could not be predicted, as would have been possible in the large-scale world. Thus there remained a basic 'uncertainty' in any such determination, and Heisenberg was able to postulate the scale of this 'indeterminacy' – it was given by the dimension of Planck's quantum constant. Now, almost thirty years after this enigmatic number had appeared, unbidden and unwanted, in Planck's formula, its fundamental significance stood suddenly revealed. It marked the upper limit below which any statement on events had lost its physical meaning.

The question whether an electron was a particle or a wave had also lost its meaning. The diffuse ring which wave mechanics had substituted for the precise Bohr orbit simply meant that the electron was to be found somewhere within this shadowy pattern. But to ask exactly where it was would be a question without physical meaning. All that can be said is that the electron will more probably be in the strong part of the pattern than in its fuzzy rim. However, this is now a statement of probability and not of certainty. The same argument can be applied to the riddle of radioactive decay. In the nucleus of the radium atom, a constituent particle has a small, but finite, probability of finding itself outside the confining wall of the nucleus, which means that the nucleus has disintegrated.

Rutherford's atom model, with minute particles coursing through empty space, had given a severe jolt to the classical concept of solid matter. Its transformation into a diffuse wave pattern had made things even worse. These worries, however, were completely eclipsed by Heisenberg's uncertainty relation. Determinacy, the singular connection of cause and effect, was rightly regarded as the rock on which natural philosophy was built, and for the moment it seemed as if this safe basis had been taken away. On the other hand, the laws of classical physics had been found to hold for centuries, but it was now doubtful whether the same certainty of prediction could be maintained when dealing with atoms. In the end, however, causality was saved by Max Born when he pointed out that the diffuse pattern represented a statistical probability of finding a particle. While it was true that we will have to remain forever ignorant of the position and speed of any single electron, we can be certain of strict laws as long as our observations refer to a large number of particles. In other words, the validity of all our laws of nature is based on the fact that they are statistical ones in which the behaviour of one particular event is immaterial. While it is impossible to predict when one particular atom of radium will disintegrate, it can be said with absolute certainty that, in even a small grain of radium, half of the atoms will have broken up in 1,620 years.

This fact that causality is saved in large-scale physics does not mean that quantum physics obeys the same laws – far from it. There is, for instance, the problem of identity. When two billiard balls collide we can observe the rebound, and after the collision we still can identify ball *A* which is white and ball *B* which is black. The same cannot be done with two electrons, because one electron is completely identical with any other electron, and for this reason we can never label them. So there is no point in saying that on collision they have rebounded. We can say with equal justification that they have passed through each other, since

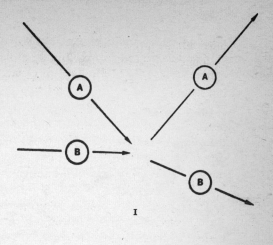

I

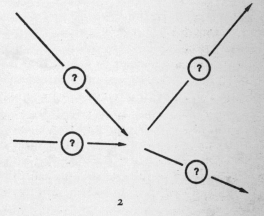

Fig. 23. According to quantum mechanics it is impossible to distinguish between individual elementary particles. When two billiard balls A and B collide (1) we can say which is which after the impact. The same is not possible in the case of two electrons (2) since they have no identity. They may have ricocheted or passed through each other.

2

we will be quite unable to decide between these two cases. This lack of identity leads to a strange consequence which is completely missing in classical physics. Two hydrogen atoms, each having just one electron, can share these electrons between them and thereby form a hydrogen molecule. This continual exchange of electrons results in a strong force between the atoms for which there exists no counterpart in our large-scale everyday world. However hard we might try, we cannot visualize this process, which is peculiar to atomic dimensions and beyond our experience.

This exchange force as the basis of chemical binding found its counterpart in the explanation of the immensely strong force holding the atomic

nucleus together. Nuclei consist of two kinds of particle: protons that
have positive electric charge, and neutrons which have no charge. Thus
there can be no electric force that binds them together. Some other
agency had to be invoked, as for instance a so far undiscovered particle
which is exchanged between proton and neutron. This was discovered
twelve years after its existence had been postulated by a theoretician.
Now the whites had been scooped, for the theoretician who predicted
it was a Japanese, Hideki Yukawa.

The exchange force, so fundamentally important for understanding
the mechanics of chemical and nuclear binding, did not remain the only
chapter of quantum physics which completely defies imagination, and
to which the key is mathematics alone. When Pauli first talked about the
classically non-describable features of atomic dimension, he had in mind
a property which became known as the 'spin' of the electron. Spin is
known in large-scale classical physics, as for instance the spin of the
earth around its axis, or the spin of a flywheel. However, it soon turned
out that electronic spin had another quite different and very far-reaching
significance. In our world of observation the rotation of a flywheel will
not affect the rotation of another flywheel, but the spin of an electron
governs the spins of any other electron by prohibiting it from having
exactly the same energy value, a state of affairs which we have to accept
but which we cannot explain. Since then, many other properties of
sub-atomic particles have been discovered which we can only describe
mathematically and for which we can find no counterpart whatever in
our world of experience. Since even theoreticians cannot converse
entirely in mathematical equations, convenient names for these properties have had to be invented, but care has been taken that these should
not conjure up false similarities with familiar concepts. We therefore
now know particles which have 'strangeness', 'colour', and even 'charm'
and 'gentleness'.

However, the odd and seemingly esoteric nature of quantum concepts
has not prevented them from becoming powerful tools for practical
prediction. Using ideas like these, Bohr and Wheeler suggested that a
hypothetical atomic nucleus of atomic weight 239, not existing on earth,
might become an extremely efficient agent for the liberation of atomic
energy. Shortly afterwards it was created by bombarding uranium with
neutrons, and was named plutonium.

With our fossil fuels running low, atomic energy and, particularly, a
reactor that 'breeds' plutonium are at present the great hope for stilling
the energy hunger of our technological world. But even before this

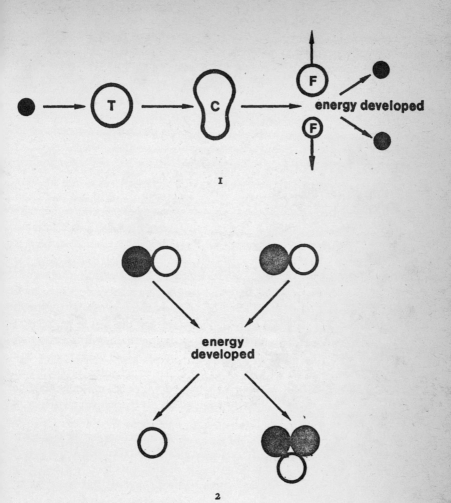

Fig. 24. In fission energy is gained by breaking up heavy nuclei (1). A neutron hits a heavy target nucleus (T) which then becomes an unstable compound nucleus (C). This breaks up after a very short time into two smaller nuclei (F, F) and a number of neutrons which, in turn, can cause further fissions. In fusion (2) energy is developed by building up heavier nuclei from very light ones.

juncture has been reached, the power of the nucleus has brought about a change in our society which may be of greater importance than any development in human affairs during the past five thousand years. The successful development of the atomic bomb had remained a well guarded secret, and in August 1945 the news of the holocaust of Hiroshima and Nagasaki burst on the war-weary world which had just been numbed by the cold-blooded murder of six million innocent men, women and children in German extermination camps. The prospect of still further deaths on an unprecedented scale, reinforced by the clamour of mindless politicians and trigger-happy generals for a 'pre-emptive strike', stunned the peoples of all nations. Apprehension was only heightened when, in less than a decade, the atomic bomb was succeeded by an incomparably more destructive weapon, the hydrogen bomb.

Sabre-rattling and dark hints, born of still darker fears, continued for some years, and then all this died down – a change had occurred which went practically unnoticed by the general public. The stage had been reached when both superpowers were in possession of the 'doomsday machine'. It had been realized quite early by scientists that the effect of such a super-explosion can be enhanced in a still more macabre manner by adding long-lived radioactive substances. Scattered by the original explosion, these can render large tracts of land uninhabitable for hundreds of years. It is therefore a foregone conclusion that in any nuclear war the losing side could let off a suitable number of such 'dirty' bombs – it does not even matter where – and poison the atmosphere of the globe, thus creating a gigantic Doomsday.

Contemplation of this eventuality is, by definition, profitless, since there is no point in debating a state devoid of future. The alternative is, of course, the abolition of war which, however, is unlikely to be a sudden and painless process, particularly since it means giving up an ancient tradition long regarded as both honourable and indispensable. On the other hand, we are already witnessing the degradation of combat by restricting it to areas less 'sensitive' than the territories of the great powers, and conducting it with almost clinically controlled, precisely measured doses of non-nuclear arms shipments to carefully chosen 'theatres of war'. It is to be expected that slowly but surely both actors and spectators will grow tired of it, and seriously contemplate living together and selling each other food and consumer goods instead of obsolescent weapons. If, as one begins to suspect, natural philosophy has abolished war – even if it be by waving a very big stick – it might be called a success in the exercise of enforced morality.

Epilogue

Between 8 and 9.30 on the morning of Sunday, 7 December 1941, Japanese torpedo-carrying aircraft destroyed the United States Pacific Fleet at its base in Pearl Harbor. Reaction in the world varied from jubilation among the Axis powers to disgust and horror in America and England at this treacherous blow, struck while Japanese diplomats still sat at the negotiating table in Washington. However, neither side seemed aware of the historic significance of the event. An Asiatic race had struck a crippling blow against the mightiest Western power, using the white man's own weapons. The fruits of Western natural philosophy had been turned against its originators.

It can hardly be said that an Asian civilization had turned against the colonial powers in self-defence. Japan never was a colony, and was not at war with America. She had in fact herself been set on a course of global domination for several decades. In 1874 Japan had made war on China, and in the following year took from her Korea, Taiwan, the Pescadores islands, and the southern part of Manchuria. After continuous incursions into Chinese territory, this was followed by the bombardment of Shanghai, the occupation of the whole of Manchuria, and of large parts of inner Mongolia. She then used the preoccupation of Europe with World War II to march into China proper, occupying the whole eastern half of the country. Japan made it quite clear that the object was to gain food, raw materials and 'living space' for her overpopulated industrialized country.

Using her superior technological potential against China, and later in Southeast Asia and the Pacific, Japan demonstrated the obvious fact that domination of less developed nations simply stems from the employment of this power, and that it is not a prerogative of the white race. It was by exercising the strength conferred upon man through his harnessing of the forces of nature that China was brought to her knees, not through an innate wish for domination. The Japanese example conclusively shows that, once the armoury created by natural philosophy is at hand, domination tends to follow. This may not be a pleasant reflection upon the moral fibre of man, but it certainly exonerates the white race from operating its exclusive application. Science and technology in the hands of man – and this means any man who has their use – confer on him an unprecedented degree of power over his neighbours. It appears that mankind has so far not found the means or the moral strength to resist the temptation of domination of man over man. Let it be remembered that by far the greatest exercise of this capacity to conquer has been by whites making war on whites. The only difference as far as the other races are concerned is that their failure to develop technology made them defenceless, and therefore easy targets for attack. As a result, the casualties of the operation, even if we include the slave trade, were much smaller than those of the whites fighting each other.

The Japanese expansion makes rather less convincing the argument so beloved by pontificating churchmen, committed sociologists and other professional do-gooders, that colonialism springs from the greed and moral turpitude of the white man. Even they cannot seriously believe that, if his scientists were to provide an African Redeemer or a Muslim Mahdi with the technology to supply the means of domination, such men would desist from using them in the same manner as the whites or the Japanese. Unbridled lust for power and its ruthless exercise show a remarkable impartiality, irrespective of race or colour.

It is generally held that race or colour make no difference to native human intelligence, and I for one would not hope to win in a mental ability test against a member of the Hanlin Academy or of a Sanskrit college. The same state of affairs must equally have obtained five or six hundred years ago, when the whites embarked on their pursuit of natural philosophy. It can hardly be a charge against the white race that they developed their own brand of philosophy and that it proved successful. They were not very secretive about it, and even offered it freely. If the other civilizations took no interest in it, apportioning guilt becomes a somewhat pointless exercise.

In fact it is a curious feature of colonialism that the white conquerors pushed their domination to the extent of insisting that, together with Christianity, the other races should embrace and even practice the benefits of science. For a long time they politely declined, and only those who went out to spread the gospel of natural philosophy can gauge the full impact of the consumer resistance on the part of peoples who pre-

ferred their own mode of life. The spread of science outside the white
orbit is a very recent development which still has not taken firm root
except in the Far East. We must leave out black Africa since it chose to
remain in an agricultural village society, never creating proper urban
centres, the institution of a state, or the development of a script, and
therefore was incapable of producing science. The term 'chose to remain'
has been applied purposely since, if they had wished to, Africans could
have copied all these achievements from Egypt, with which they were
in close contact five thousand years ago. In fact, until this day, native
attempts at controlling the forces of nature have remained at the magic
level of the fetish priest and the medicine man. The very recent scientific
effort in black Africa is a meagre graft that has not yet seriously taken.

Until the beginning of the twentieth century, science in the great
civilizations of the East remained on the medieval level that obtained in
Europe before the onset of the Renaissance. Such advances as were made
in the five hundred years since 1400 did not accelerate beyond the pace
characteristic of the West before that time. Life in their cultural orbits
progressed as ours would have done, had it not been for the rise of
natural philosophy. Traditional Indian science, as well as the influence
brought upon it by the Muslims, was chiefly concerned with mathematics and astronomy. A number of impressive observatories were built
in the eighteenth century, but they were mainly devoted to astrological
purposes and, although their size and careful lay-out permitted accurate
data to be obtained, no attempt was made to turn them to scientific use.
Science departments in universities introduced by the British were a
fairly late development which, early in this century, were augmented by
a number of scientific institutions, all again on the Western pattern and
sponsored by Western nations. With the departure of the colonizing
power, the average scientific standard at Indian and Pakistani universities
has not necessarily increased. Altogether, the impression is gained that
foreign aid in science and technology has been a mixed blessing. Except
in a few centres of excellence which can be counted on the fingers of one
hand, natural philosophy has not yet taken root in India. There is a
marked tendency to import the wherewithals, ranging from instruments
to whole steel plants, from abroad rather than trying to produce them
locally. Possibly the example of the centres of excellence will eventually
result in indigenous scientific growth which need not be supported by
frequent study visits to the West, but it would be foolish to assume that
the spirit of science at present means anything to the Indian man in the
street or in the village.

Japan, on the other hand, has rapidly developed into a technological nation in the Western sense. Her progress has been breathtaking, though for most of the way it has consisted of closely copying the Western model in schools, universities and factories. Japan's strength in the past century has been unlimited and highly disciplined manpower at a comparatively low living standard. Prior to the opening up of the country in 1867, technological skills were limited to the manufacture of steel for both sword blades and primitive firearms, the latter being a Portuguese importation. If anything, science was discouraged by the policy of the Tokugawa Shogunate, which maintained the bakufu, a military government on feudal lines, to keep the country isolated from the West. Whatever we may think of the wisdom of Tokugawa policy, Japan's meteoric rise to technological eminence, and her military successes, have led to new problems. First of all, her technology is beginning to be not merely imitative of Western example. It is perhaps too early to judge whether Japan's contribution has as yet become original, but her drive and competence make this a distinct possibility. The second factor is that, having broken her isolation and been drawn into the vortex of Western development, she is beginning to pay the penalty – Japan is poorer than anyone else in energy supply. In spite of earlier contacts, for the great majority of Japanese the change into the Western way of life is only one generation old, and the security of their own culture is a living memory. Who knows whether they will not try to take refuge in it?

There is probably no place on earth where – in spite of great political upheavals – tradition is as deeply rooted as in China. When her emperors a few hundred years ago found no other use for the Jesuit scientists than the making of clocks and the design of water pumps for fountains, they were convinced that they acted from a position of strength, and they meant moral strength. They may have been right, but their underestimation of Western science was an error of judgment for which they had to pay dearly. China's present attitude was made abundantly clear when Mao Tse-tung told me that he admired Western science, and that China had to make good her backwardness in this field. She certainly has in a very few years gone a long way to repair this shortcoming. However, China is clearly determined not to repeat the Japanese example of assimilating the Western social patterns – not even Soviet socialism. China's new rulers have recognized the fact that competitiveness in the twentieth century is based on science, but they seem to regard it as a phenomenon which can be separated from the European cultural heritage that was its cradle. They avidly and very successfully absorb the fruits of Western scientific thought, but they remain remarkably uninterested in the historical development of it. Modern science in China started with the first course at Peking university in 1920. Its Western pattern of scientific education was not basically changed when, after 1949, it was much extended on the Soviet model. Soon, however, certain changes were introduced, and then a complete rethinking took place through the cultural revolution. Its aim was to recast the educational system into a specifically Chinese mould designed to fit the social and economic requirements of their own country.

The problems facing China are, indeed, unique. A population approaching a thousand million, which until quite recently was largely illiterate, is faced with a common but comparatively difficult script of ideograms, and at the same time beset by a multitude of tonal languages. Any attempt to create out of this a society that is competitive in the twentieth century has had to concentrate on mass education at the lowest school level, and to think out its policy very carefully; and this has indeed been the chief aim of the cultural revolution. Next to the primary task of teaching in a common language, for which a modernized form of Mandarin has been chosen, basic science has become the backbone of education. The approach to this, however, is quite different from the Western pattern. It all starts from a strictly practical angle, with the theoretical explanation to follow later, and then only as far as is necessary for the task in hand. Agricultural classes are held in the rice field, where training in the selection of seed grain slowly merges into plant genetics. Operation and servicing of tractors and electromotors come first, with basic thermodynamics or electrical theory left, if needed, to a later stage. This makes a combination of school and production a necessity rather than an ideological object, and it is from this angle that we should judge the close connection of all primary schools with factories. The final result of this immense scheme will be a vast population to whom the basic logic of scientific reasoning will not be a set teaching subject but second nature.

The burden of this book has been to show that the consistent development of natural philosophy has given to the white race the power of domination over others. It has been an exclusively Western endeavour, arising as an intellectual effort out of a specific cultural pattern. The deep significance of the Chinese experiment lies in a subtle divorce of science from its Western heritage. It is tacitly assumed that the growth of science is a common feature of human society, irrespective of race. The Chinese system lays emphasis on their ancient method of the child helping its parents in the field, and the value of tradition is stressed in those scientific methods where China has been pre-eminent, as for instance the astonishing successes achieved with acupuncture. The Chinese have always been conscious of the antiquity – and let them be honest, of the superiority – of their culture and way of life. Communist ideology has not changed their name for their country – the Realm of the Centre. Perhaps it is only natural that they look upon the Western success of natural philosophy as one of those fluctuations through which the history of man passes and which accidentally happened to favour, temporarily, the whites. Possibly they are right, and this would explain their lack of interest in the European history of scientific thought.

Whatever interpretation the Chinese will give to the creation and growth of natural philosophy, it is bound to be rather more informed than the arguments of our own latter-day philosophers who forever question whether science and technology are 'good' for mankind. Here we are back to the number of angels dancing on the point of a needle – it is a useless question. Man is not just a naked ape but a creature whose evolutionary significance lies in the large frontal lobes of our brain where reason is concocted. It was an entirely new step in life where for the first time reason, a new invention of nature, has made the human being more competitive than species which rely on instinct only. *Homo sapiens* represents the first, and as yet pretty incomplete, step in this new direction, and science is a major feature of it. To argue whether it was a good thing to develop science is about as profitable as to command the genes to stop mutating – they won't. Science is with us not just because we have invented it but because it is a phase in human biological evolution. Perhaps the main problem is, that having been given reason, we take ourselves too seriously. As far as the phenomenon of life is concerned we are still puppets on a stage, enacting a play of which we do not know the plot. Nevertheless, that little scene called natural philosophy has given us much satisfaction and we need not really be ashamed of it. Even if the white race is destined to step down, the play is likely to go on, sustained if necessary through an increasing addition to the cast by Indian, Japanese and Chinese Nobel laureates.

70, 71 Pioneering physicists of the new century. *Left*, Ernest Rutherford (1871–1937), later Baron Rutherford of Nelson. *Right*, Marie Curie, the discoverer of radium.

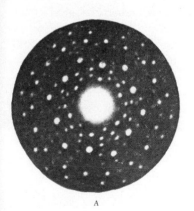
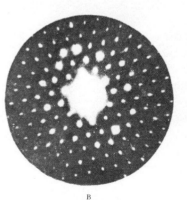

A   B

72 Similar diffraction patterns produced (a) by electromagnetic waves (X-rays) and (b) by a beam of electrons.

73 Loading dummy fuel containers into the prototype fast nuclear reactor at Dounreay, Caithness, Scotland.

74, 75 Science and the Third World. *Above*, the university of science and technology at Kumasi, Ghana, one of Nkrumah's prestige projects. *Right*, an Ashanti student in the physics laboratory at Kumasi.

76, 77 *Opposite*, Jantar Mantar, Delhi. This native Indian observatory was built in 1725 by Jai Singh, but served mainly astrological purposes. *Right*, Western science in India is given a suitably modern appearance: the Tata Institute for fundamental research, Bombay.

78 An Indian girl observing tracks of fundamental particles, using a special microscope.

79 A Japanese prototype vehicle for a magnetically levitated train designed to achieve a speed of 500 m.p.h.

80 An early Chinese astronomical instrument. Originally made for the latitude of Peking, it now stands at Nanking Observatory.

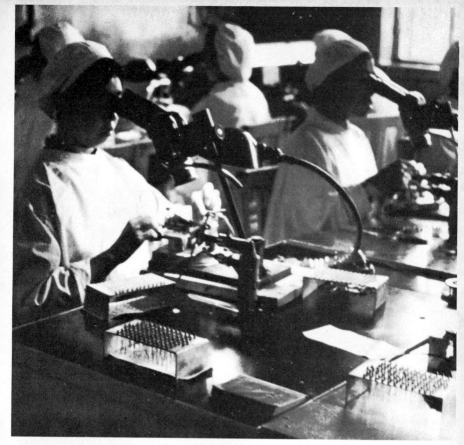

81, 82 Transistor production in Maoist China. *Above*, girls at work in a Peking factory. *Left* a technician displays germanium single crystal for transistors.

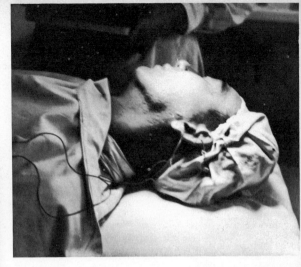

83, 84, 85 Science and the cultural revolution. *Above*, acupuncture anaesthesia in a modern Peking hospital. *Left*, a girl doing lorry repair work at her school. *Below*, a biology lesson takes place in the rice field.

Select Bibliography

Since this is not a scholarly text but a book addressed to the general reader, only a short list of standard reference works and biographies is given.

Andrade E. N. da C., *Sir Isaac Newton*, London, 1954; New York, 1958.

Armitage A., *John Kepler*, London, 1966; New York, 1967.
Copernicus, the Founder of Modern Astronomy, London, 1938; Cranbury, New Jersey, 1971.

Bernal J. D., *Science in History* (4 vols.), Harmondsworth and Cambridge, Mass., 1969.

Butterfield H., *The Origins of Modern Science*, New York, 1965; London, 1968.

Clark R. W., *Einstein*, London, 1973.

Campbell L., and W. Garnett, *The Life of James Clerk Maxwell*, London, 1882; New York, 1970 (repr.).

Dampier, Sir William G., *A History of Science*, Cambridge, 1942.

Derry T. K., and T. S. Williams, *A Short History of Technology*, Oxford, 1960.

Dijksterhuis E. J., *The Mechanization of the World Picture*, Oxford, 1961.

Dreyer J. L. E., *Tycho Brahe*, Edinburgh, 1890.

Einstein A., and L. Infeld, *The Evolution of Physics*, Cambridge, 1938; New York, 1961.

Eve A. S., *Rutherford*, Cambridge, 1939.

Eves H., *History of Mathematics*, New York, 1970.

Hull L. W. H., *History and Philosophy of Science*, London, 1959.

Lyons H., *The Royal Society, 1660–1940*, Cambridge, 1944; Westport, Conn., 1968 (repr.).

Maddison R. E. W., *The Life of the Hon. Robert Boyle*, London, 1969.

Newman J. R., *The World of Mathematics* (4 vols.), London, 1960; New York, 1967.

Pannekoek A., *A History of Astronomy*, London and Totowa, N.J., 1961.

Planck M., *Scientific Autobiography*, London, 1950; Westport, Conn., 1968.

Pledge H. T., *Science Since 1500*, London, 1939.

Robinson W. and W. Adams, *The Diary of Robert Hooke (1672–1680)*, London, 1935; New York, 1968 (repr.).

Ronan C. A., *Galileo*, London, 1974.

Singer C., *A Short History of Scientific Ideas*, Oxford, 1959; Gloucester, Mass., 1960.

Singer C. E. J. (Holmyard), A. R. Hall, and T. J. Williams, *A History of Technology* (5 vols.), Oxford, 1954–58.

Sprat T., *History of the Royal Society*, St Louis, Missouri, 1938 (repr.).

Stimson D., *Scientists and Amateurs*, London, 1949; Westport, Conn., 1974.

Taylor F. Sherwood, *A Short History of Science*, London, 1939; New York, 1963.

Thompson S. P., *Life of Lord Kelvin* (2 vols.), London, 1910; New York, 1974 (repr.).

Weld C. R., *History of the Royal Society* (2 vols.), Cambridge, 1848.

Williams L. P., *Michael Faraday*, London, 1965; New York, 1971.

List of Illustrations

Index

PHOTO ACKNOWLEDGMENTS

Author: 3, 4, 5, 6, 7, 8, 17, 30, 32, 33, 74, 75, 76, 77, 78, 80, 81, 82, 83, 84, 85
Japanese National Railways: 79
Library of Congress: 65
Marconi Company: 69
Mansell-Alinari: 28
Mas: 1

National Galleries of Scotland: 36
Radio Times Hulton Picture Library: 55, 71
Ronan Picture Library: 52, 57, 58, 68
Science Museum: 29, 45, 59, 61, 62, 63, 64, 66
United Kingdom Atomic Energy Authority: 73